IN ASSOCIATION WITH

✕SQA

HODDER
GIBSON
Model Papers
WITH ANSWERS

PLUS: Official SQA Specimen Paper
With Answers

Advanced Higher for CfE
Biology

2015 Specimen Question Paper
& Model Papers

HODDER
GIBSON
AN HACHETTE UK COMPANY

This book contains the official 2015 SQA Specimen Question Paper for Advanced Higher for CfE Biology, with associated SQA approved answers modified from the official marking instructions that accompany the paper.

In addition the book contains model papers, together with answers, plus study skills advice. These papers, some of which may include a limited number of previously published SQA questions, have been specially commissioned by Hodder Gibson, and have been written by experienced senior teachers and examiners in line with the new Advanced Higher for CfE syllabus and assessment outlines, Spring 2015. This is not SQA material but has been devised to provide further practice for Advanced Higher for CfE examinations in 2016 and beyond.

Hodder Gibson is grateful to the copyright holders, as credited on the final page of the Answer Section, for permission to use their material. Every effort has been made to trace the copyright holders and to obtain their permission for the use of copyright material. Hodder Gibson will be happy to receive information allowing us to rectify any error or omission in future editions.

Hachette UK's policy is to use papers that are natural, renewable and recyclable products and made from wood grown in sustainable forests. The logging and manufacturing processes are expected to conform to the environmental regulations of the country of origin.

Orders: please contact Bookpoint Ltd, 130 Park Drive, Milton Park, Abingdon, Oxon OX14 4SE. Telephone: (44) 01235 827720. Fax: (44) 01235 400454. Lines are open 9.00–5.00, Monday to Saturday, with a 24-hour message answering service. Visit our website at www.hoddereducation.co.uk. Hodder Gibson can be contacted direct on: Tel: 0141 848 1609; Fax: 0141 889 6315; email: hoddergibson@hodder.co.uk

This collection first published in 2016 by
Hodder Gibson, an imprint of Hodder Education,
An Hachette UK Company
2a Christie Street
Paisley PA1 1NB

Typeset by Aptara, Inc.

Printed in the UK

A catalogue record for this title is available from the British Library

ISBN: 978-1-4718-6017-1

3 2 1

2017 2016

Introduction

Study Skills – what you need to know to pass exams!

Pause for thought

Many students might skip quickly through a page like this. After all, we all know how to revise. Do you really though?

Think about this:

"IF YOU ALWAYS DO WHAT YOU ALWAYS DO, YOU WILL ALWAYS GET WHAT YOU HAVE ALWAYS GOT."

Do you like the grades you get? Do you want to do better? If you get full marks in your assessment, then that's great! Change nothing! This section is just to help you get that little bit better than you already are.

There are two main parts to the advice on offer here. The first part highlights fairly obvious things but which are also very important. The second part makes suggestions about revision that you might not have thought about but which WILL help you.

Part 1

DOH! It's so obvious but …

Start revising in good time

Don't leave it until the last minute – this will make you panic.

Make a revision timetable that sets out work time AND play time.

Sleep and eat!

Obvious really, and very helpful. Avoid arguments or stressful things too – even games that wind you up. You need to be fit, awake and focused!

Know your place!

Make sure you know exactly **WHEN and WHERE** your exams are.

Know your enemy!

Make sure you know what to expect in the exam.

How is the paper structured?

How much time is there for each question?

What types of question are involved?

Which topics seem to come up time and time again?

Which topics are your strongest and which are your weakest?

Are all topics compulsory or are there choices?

Learn by DOING!

There is no substitute for past papers and practice papers – they are simply essential! Tackling this collection of papers and answers is exactly the right thing to be doing as your exams approach.

Part 2

People learn in different ways. Some like low light, some bright. Some like early morning, some like evening or night. Some prefer warm, some prefer cold. But everyone uses their BRAIN and the brain works when it is active. Passive learning – sitting gazing at notes – is the most INEFFICIENT way to learn anything. Below you will find tips and ideas for making your revision more effective and maybe even more enjoyable. What follows gets your brain active, and active learning works!

Activity 1 – Stop and review

Step 1

When you have done no more than 5 minutes of revision reading STOP!

Step 2

Write a heading in your own words which sums up the topic you have been revising.

Step 3

Write a summary of what you have revised in no more than two sentences. Don't fool yourself by saying, "I know it, but I cannot put it into words". That just means you don't know it well enough. If you cannot write your summary, revise that section again, knowing that you must write a summary at the end of it. Many of you will have notebooks full of blue/black ink writing. Many of the pages will not be especially attractive or memorable so try to liven them up a bit with colour as you are reviewing and rewriting. **This is a great memory aid, and memory is the most important thing.**

Activity 2 – Use technology!

Why should everything be written down? Have you thought about "mental" maps, diagrams, cartoons and colour to help you learn? And rather than write down notes, why not record your revision material?

What about having a text message revision session with friends? Keep in touch with them to find out how and what they are revising and share ideas and questions.

Why not make a video diary where you tell the camera what you are doing, what you think you have learned and what you still have to do? No one has to see or hear it, but the process of having to organise your thoughts in a formal way to explain something is a very important learning practice.

Be sure to make use of electronic files. You could begin to summarise your class notes. Your typing might be slow, but it will get faster and the typed notes will be easier to read than the scribbles in your class notes. Try to add different fonts and colours to make your work stand out. You can easily Google relevant pictures, cartoons and diagrams which you can copy and paste to make your work more attractive and **MEMORABLE**.

Activity 3 – This is it. Do this and you will know lots!

Step 1

In this task you must be very honest with yourself! Find the SQA syllabus for your subject (www.sqa.org.uk). Look at how it is broken down into main topics called MANDATORY knowledge. That means stuff you MUST know.

Step 2

BEFORE you do ANY revision on this topic, write a list of everything that you already know about the subject. It might be quite a long list but you only need to write it once. It shows you all the information that is already in your long-term memory so you know what parts you do not need to revise!

Step 3

Pick a chapter or section from your book or revision notes. Choose a fairly large section or a whole chapter to get the most out of this activity.

With a buddy, use Skype, Facetime, Twitter or any other communication you have, to play the game "If this is the answer, what is the question?". For example, if you are revising Geography and the answer you provide is "meander", your buddy would have to make up a question like "What is the word that describes a feature of a river where it flows slowly and bends often from side to side?".

Make up 10 "answers" based on the content of the chapter or section you are using. Give this to your buddy to solve while you solve theirs.

Step 4

Construct a wordsearch of at least 10 × 10 squares. You can make it as big as you like but keep it realistic. Work together with a group of friends. Many apps allow you to make wordsearch puzzles online. The words and phrases can go in any direction and phrases can be split. Your puzzle must only contain facts linked to the topic you are revising. Your task is to find 10 bits of information to hide in your puzzle, but you must not repeat information that you used in Step 3. DO NOT show where the words are. Fill up empty squares with random letters. Remember to keep a note of where your answers are hidden but do not show your friends. When you have a complete puzzle, exchange it with a friend to solve each other's puzzle.

Step 5

Now make up 10 questions (not "answers" this time) based on the same chapter used in the previous two tasks. Again, you must find NEW information that you have not yet used. Now it's getting hard to find that new information! Again, give your questions to a friend to answer.

Step 6

As you have been doing the puzzles, your brain has been actively searching for new information. Now write a NEW LIST that contains only the new information you have discovered when doing the puzzles. Your new list is the one to look at repeatedly for short bursts over the next few days. Try to remember more and more of it without looking at it. After a few days, you should be able to add words from your second list to your first list as you increase the information in your long-term memory.

FINALLY! Be inspired...

Make a list of different revision ideas and beside each one write **THINGS I HAVE** tried, **THINGS I WILL** try and **THINGS I MIGHT** try. Don't be scared of trying something new.

And remember – "FAIL TO PREPARE AND PREPARE TO FAIL!"

Advanced Higher Biology

The practice papers in this book give an overall and comprehensive coverage of assessment of **Knowledge** and skills of **Scientific Inquiry** for the new CfE Advanced Higher Biology.

We recommend that you download and print a copy of the CfE Advanced Higher Biology Course Assessment Specification (CAS) pages 8–17 from the SQA website at www.sqa.org.uk.

The Course

The CfE Advanced Higher Biology Course consists of three National Units. These are Cells and Proteins, Organisms and Evolution, and Investigative Biology. In each of the Units you will be assessed on your ability to demonstrate and apply knowledge of Biology and to demonstrate and apply skills of scientific inquiry.

You must also complete a project, the purpose of which is to allow you to carry out an in-depth investigation of a Biology topic and produce a project–report. You will also take a Course examination.

How the Course is graded

To achieve a Course award for CfE Advanced Higher Biology you must pass all three National Unit Assessments which will be assessed by your school or college on a pass or fail basis. The grade you get depends on the following two Course assessments, which are set and graded by SQA.

1. The project is worth 25% of the grade and is marked out of 30 marks. The majority of the marks will be awarded for applying scientific inquiry skills. The other marks will be awarded for applying related knowledge and understanding.

2. A written Course examination is worth the remaining 75% of the grade. The examination is marked out of 90 marks, 60–70 of which are for the demonstration and application of knowledge with the balance for skills of scientific inquiry.

This book should help you practise the examination part! To pass CfE Advanced Higher Biology with a C grade you will need about 50% of the 120 marks available for the project and the Course examination combined. For a B you will need roughly 60% and, for an A, roughly 70% of the marks available.

The Course examination

The Course examination is a single question paper divided into two sections.

- The first section is an objective test with 25 multiple choice items worth 25 marks.

- The second section is a mix of restricted and extended response questions worth between 1 and 9 marks each for a total of 65 marks. The majority of the marks test knowledge, with an emphasis on the application of knowledge. The remainder test the application of scientific inquiry, analysis and problem solving skills. The first question is usually an extensive data question and there are two extended response questions, one for about 4–5 marks and the other for about 8–10 marks – the longer extended response question will normally have a choice and is usually the last question in the paper.

Altogether, there are 90 marks and you will have 2 hours and 30 minutes to complete the paper. The majority of the marks will be straightforward and linked to grade C but some questions are more demanding and are linked to grade A.

General hints and tips

You should have a copy of the Course Assessment Specification (CAS) for CfE Advanced Higher Biology but, if you haven't got one, make sure to download it from the SQA website. It is worth spending some time looking at this document, as it indicates what you can be tested on in your examination.

This book contains four practice CfE Advanced Higher Biology examination papers. One is the SQA specimen paper and there are three further Hodder Gibson model papers. Each model paper has been carefully assembled to be as similar as possible to a typical CfE Advanced Higher Biology examination paper. Notice how similar they all are in the way in which they are laid out and the types of question they ask – your own Course examination is going to be very similar as well, so the value of these papers is obvious! Each paper can be attempted in its entirety, or groups of questions on a particular topic or skill area can be attempted. If you are trying a whole examination paper from this book, give yourself a maximum of 2 hours and 30 minutes to complete it. The questions in each paper are laid out roughly in Unit order. Make sure that you spend time in using the answer section to mark your own work – it is especially useful if you can get someone to help you with this.

The marking instructions give acceptable answers with alternatives. You could even grade your work on an A–D basis. The following hints and tips are related to examination techniques as well as avoiding common mistakes. Remember that if you hit problems with a question, you should ask your teacher for help.

Section 1

25 multiple-choice items **25 marks**

- Answer on a grid.
- Do not spend more than 30 minutes on this section.
- Some individual questions might take longer to answer than others – this is quite normal and make sure you use scrap paper if a calculation or any working is needed.
- Some questions can be answered instantly – again, this is normal.
- Do not leave blanks – complete the grid for each question as you work through.
- Try to answer each question in your head without looking at the options. If your answer is there you are home and dry!
- If you are not certain, it is sometimes best to choose the answer that seemed most attractive on first reading the answer options.
- If you are guessing, try to eliminate options before making your guess. If you can eliminate three, you will be left with the correct answer even if you do not recognise it!

Section 2

Restricted and extended response **65 marks**

- Spend about 2 hours on this section.
- A clue to your answer length is the mark allocation – questions restricted to 1 mark can be quite short. If there are 2–3 marks available, your answer will need to be extended and may well have two, three or even four parts.
- The questions are usually laid out in Unit sequence but remember that some questions are designed to cover more than one Unit.
- The C-type questions usually start with "State", "Identify", "Give" or "Name" and often need only a single sentence in response. They will usually be for 1 mark each.
- Questions that begin with "Explain", "Suggest" and "Describe" are usually A-type questions and are likely to have more than one part to the full answer. You will usually have to write a sentence or two and there may be 2 or even 3 marks available.
- Make sure you read over the question twice **before** trying to answer – there will be very important information within the question and underlining or highlighting key words is good technique.
- Using abbreviations like DNA and ATP is fine. The CfE Advanced Higher Biology Course Assessment Specification (CAS) will give you the acceptable abbreviations.

- Don't worry if the questions are in unfamiliar contexts, that's the idea! Just keep calm and read the questions carefully.
- In the large data question (Q1), it is good technique to read the whole stem and then skim the data groups before starting to answer any of the parts.
- In the large data question (Q1), be aware that the first piece of data presented should give the main theme of the question.
- In experimental questions, you must be aware of the different classes of variables, why controls are needed and how reliability and validity might be improved. It is worth spending time on these ideas – they are essential and will come up year after year.
- Note that information which is additional to the main stem may be given within a question part – if it's there, you will need it!
- If instructions in the question ask you to refer to specific groups of data, follow these and don't go beyond them.
- Remember that a conclusion can be seen from data, whereas an explanation will usually require you to supply some background knowledge as well.
- Note that in your answer, you may be asked to "use data to…" – it is essential that you do this.
- Remember to "use values from the graph" when describing graphical information in words, if you are asked to do so.
- Look out for graphs with two Y-axes – these need extra special concentration and anyone can make a mistake!
- In numerical answers, it's good technique to show working and supply units.
- Answers to calculations will not usually have more than two decimal places.
- You should round any numerical answers as appropriate, but two decimal places should be acceptable.
- Ensure that you take error bars into account when evaluating the effects of treatments.
- Do not leave blanks. Always have a go, using the language in the question if you can.

Good luck!

Remember that the rewards for passing Advanced Higher Biology are well worth it! Your pass will help you get the future you want for yourself. In the exam, be confident in your own ability. If you're not sure how to answer a question, trust your instincts and just give it a go anyway.

Keep calm and don't panic! GOOD LUCK!

National
Qualifications
SPECIMEN ONLY

SQ02/AH/02

Biology
Section 1—Questions

Date — Not applicable

Duration — 2 hours 30 minutes

Instructions for the completion of Section 1 are given on *Page two* of your question and answer booklet SQ02/H/01.

Record your answers on the answer grid on *Page three* of your question and answer booklet.

Before leaving the examination room you must give your question and answer booklet to the Invigilator; if you do not, you may lose all the marks for this paper.

SECTION 1 — 25 marks

Attempt ALL questions

1. Which of the following is a covalent bond that stabilises the tertiary structure of a protein?

   A   Disulphide bridge

   B   Hydrogen bond

   C   Ionic bond

   D   Hydrophobic interactions

2. A hydrophobic amino acid has an R group that is

   A   negatively charged

   B   positively charged

   C   not polar

   D   polar.

3. A buffered solution of four amino acids was applied to the midline of a strip of electrophoresis gel. The result of running the gel is shown below.

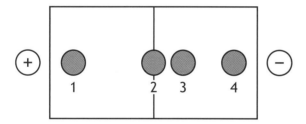

   Which of the amino acids was at its isoelectric point?

   A   1

   B   2

   C   3

   D   4

4. The table shows the number of amino acids in a particular protein and the charge of each amino acid at a certain pH.

Amino acid	Charge	Number
arginine	positive	13
aspartate	negative	9
cysteine	negative	2
histidine	positive	2
glutamate	negative	20
lysine	positive	19
tyrosine	negative	7

Assuming that each amino acid carries a single positive or negative charge, what is the protein's net charge at this pH?

A   −4

B   −38

C   +4

D   +38

5. The diagram below shows how phosphate is used to modify the conformation of an enzyme, phosphorylase, and so change its activity.

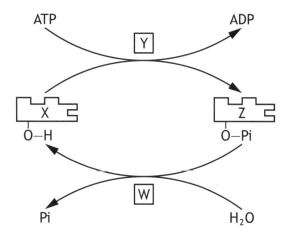

Which line in the table correctly identifies the labels?

	Kinase	Phosphatase	Phosphorylase
A	Y	Z	W
B	W	Y	Z
C	X	Y	W
D	Y	W	Z

6. The diagram below shows the distribution of protein molecules in a cell membrane.

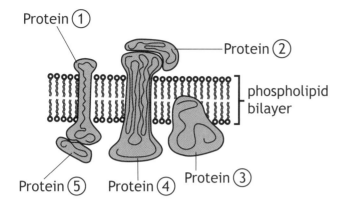

Which line in the table correctly identifies a peripheral and an integral membrane protein?

	Peripheral membrane protein	Integral membrane protein
A	1	5
B	2	1
C	3	4
D	5	2

7. The sodium-potassium pump spans the plasma membrane. Various processes involved in the active transport of sodium and potassium ions take place either inside the cell (intracellular) or outside the cell (extracellular).

Which line in the table correctly applies to the binding of potassium ions?

	Binding location of potassium ions	Conformation of transport protein
A	extracellular	not phosphorylated
B	intracellular	not phosphorylated
C	extracellular	phosphorylated
D	intracellular	phosphorylated

8. The diagram below shows a haemocytometer grid that was used to estimate the number of cells in a $10 \, cm^3$ microbial culture. The depth of the counting chamber is $0 \cdot 2 \, mm$.

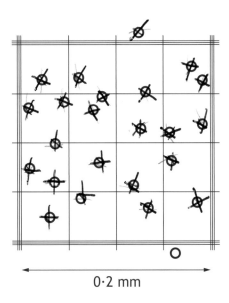

0·2 mm

The number of cells in the $10 \, cm^3$ culture was

A $2 \cdot 75 \times 10^7$

B $2 \cdot 5 \times 10^7$

C $2 \cdot 25 \times 10^7$

D $1 \cdot 6 \times 10^3$.

9. The contribution of aquaporins (AQPs) to osmosis was studied by measuring the rate of movement of radioactive water across a plasma membrane. Rates were measured in either isotonic or hypertonic external solution when the pores were either open or closed. Results are shown in the table.

External solution	Rate of water movement (units s^{-1})	
	Open AQPs	Closed AQPs
Isotonic	2·5	1·0
Hypertonic	20·0	1·8

Which of the following is the dependent variable in the experiment?

A   External solution

B   Radioactivity of water

C   Rate of water movement

D   Aquaporins

10. To which group of signalling molecules do steroid hormones belong?

    A   Extracellular hydrophobic

    B   Extracellular hydrophilic

    C   Peptide hormones

    D   Neurotransmitters

11. The following diagrams represent stages in an indirect ELISA used to detect the presence of a poisonous toxin in food samples. The test shown is positive. Identify the diagram that represents the correct sequence of events in the ELISA.

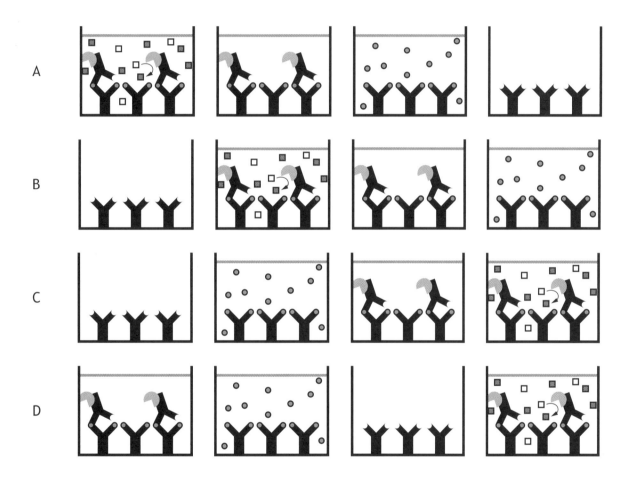

12. Identify which of the following proteins are involved in apoptosis.

    1   Caspases

    2   p53

    3   DNAses

    A   2 only

    B   1 and 2 only

    C   1 and 3 only

    D   1, 2 and 3

13. Animal cells growing in culture are found to spend 20% of their time in the G2 phase of the cell cycle. G2 lasts for 4 hours.

   If cells spend 12% of their time in the M phase, how long does this last?

   A   2 hours 4 minutes

   B   2 hours 12 minutes

   C   2 hours 24 minutes

   D   2 hours 40 minutes

14. Name the ion which is pumped across membranes by bacteriorhodopsin.

   A   Sodium

   B   Potassium

   C   Chloride

   D   Hydrogen

15. Which of the following would be true if a population's gene pool remained unaltered for many generations?

   A   Mating was random

   B   Migration was common

   C   Genetic drift had occurred

   D   Certain alleles had a selective advantage

16. Identify the line in the table that applies to r-selected species.

	many offspring produced	prolonged parental care
A	yes	yes
B	yes	no
C	no	yes
D	no	no

17. *C. elegans* is a model organism of the phylum

   A   Chordata

   B   Arthropoda

   C   Nematoda

   D   Mollusca.

18. From the following list, identify all the possible sources of DNA during horizontal gene transfer.

    1   viruses

    2   plasmids

    3   bacterial cells

    4   gametes

    A   1 and 2 only

    B   2 and 3 only

    C   1, 2 and 3 only

    D   1, 2 ,3 and 4

19. The following diagram is **drawn to scale** and indicates the position of four linked genes on a chromosome.

    W   X   Y   Z

    Identify the column in the table that gives the correct recombination frequencies for the genes in the chromosome map shown above.

Genes	Recombination frequency (%)			
	A	B	C	D
X and Z	17	19	17	15
W and Z	25	25	23	23
Y and W	19	17	15	17
Z and Y	6	8	8	6
X and W	8	6	6	8

20. The error bars on the graphs represent standard errors in the mean (SEM). Which graph shows significantly different reliable data?

A

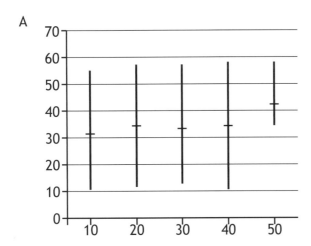

B

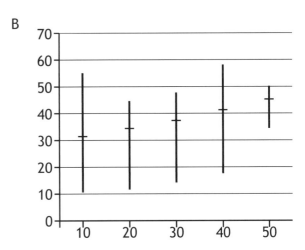

C

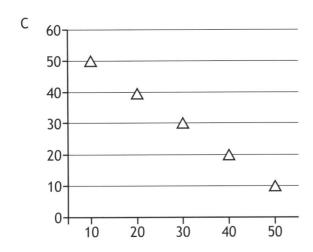

D

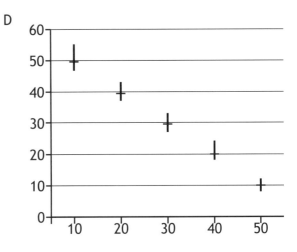

21. *Anolis* lizards are found on Caribbean islands. They feed on prey of various sizes.

    Histogram 1 shows the range of prey length eaten by *Anolis marmoratus* on the island of Jarabacoa, where there are five other *Anolis* species.

    Histogram 2 shows the range of prey length eaten by *Anolis marmoratus* on the island of Marie Galante, where it is the only *Anolis* species.

Histogram 1: Jarabacoa

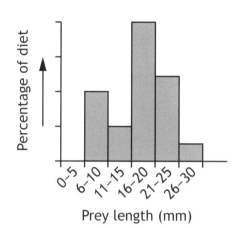

Histogram 2: Marie Galante Island

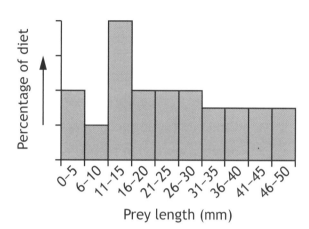

Which of the following statements could explain the different range of prey sizes eaten by *Anolis marmoratus* on the two islands?

A   Larger numbers of prey are found on Marie Galante.

B   *Anolis marmoratus* occupies its fundamental niche on Jarabacoa.

C   *Anolis marmoratus* occupies its realised niche on Marie Galante.

D   Resource partitioning takes place on Jarabacoa.

22. Herd immunity threshold is

A   The density of hosts in a population required to prevent an epidemic

B   The density of resistant hosts in a population required to prevent an epidemic

C   The density of hosts in a population required for transmission to cause an epidemic

D   The density of parasites in a population required to cause an epidemic.

23. Reverse transcriptase catalyses the production of

A   DNA from RNA

B   DNA from DNA

C   mRNA from DNA

D   tRNA from mRNA.

24. Which of the following would **not** provide long-term control of parasites following a natural disaster?

    A   Immunisation

    B   Improved sanitation

    C   Co-ordinated vector control

    D   Drug treatment of infected humans

25. The formula N = MC/R is used to estimate population size using mark and recapture data.

    N = population estimate

    M = number first captured, marked and released

    C = total number in second capture

    R = number marked in second capture

    In a survey to estimate a woodlouse population, the following data were obtained:

    Woodlice captured, marked and released   = 80

    Marked woodlice in second capture   = 24

    Unmarked woodlice in second capture   = 96

    The estimated population of the woodlice was

    A   200

    B   320

    C   400

    D   3840.

**[END OF SECTION 1. NOW ATTEMPT THE QUESTIONS IN SECTION 2
OF YOUR QUESTION AND ANSWER BOOKLET]**

Mark

AH
National Qualifications
SPECIMEN ONLY

SQ02/AH/01

Biology
Section 1 — Answer Grid and Section 2

Date — Not applicable

Duration — 2 hours 30 minutes

Fill in these boxes and read what is printed below.

Full name of centre

Town

Forename(s)

Surname

Number of seat

Date of birth

Day	Month	Year	Scottish candidate number

Total marks — 90

SECTION 1 — 25 marks

Attempt ALL questions.

Instructions for completion of Section 1 are given on *Page two*.

SECTION 2 — 65 marks

Attempt ALL questions.

Write your answers clearly in the spaces provided in this booklet. Additional space for answers and rough work is provided at the end of this booklet. If you use this space you must clearly identify the question number you are attempting. Any rough work must be written in this booklet. You should score through your rough work when you have written your final copy.

Use **blue** or **black** ink.

Before leaving the examination room you must give this booklet to the Invigilator; if you do not you may lose all the marks for this paper.

SQA
©

SECTION 1 — 25 marks

The questions for Section 1 are contained in the question paper SQ02/AH/02.
Read these and record your answers on the answer grid on *Page three* opposite.
Use **blue** or **black** ink. Do NOT use gel pens or pencil.

1. The answer to each question is **either** A, B, C or D. Decide what your answer is, then fill in the appropriate bubble (see sample question below).

2. There is **only one correct** answer to each question.

3. Any rough working should be done on the additional space for answers and rough work at the end of this booklet.

Sample Question

The thigh bone is called the

     A   humerus

     B   femur

     C   tibia

     D   fibula.

The correct answer is **B**—femur. The answer **B** bubble has been clearly filled in (see below).

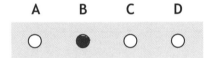

Changing an answer

If you decide to change your answer, cancel your first answer by putting a cross through it (see below) and fill in the answer you want. The answer below has been changed to **D**.

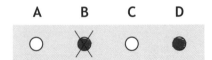

If you then decide to change back to an answer you have already scored out, put a tick (✓) to the **right** of the answer you want, as shown below:

                  or

SECTION 1 — Answer Grid

	A	B	C	D
1	○	○	○	○
2	○	○	○	○
3	○	○	○	○
4	○	○	○	○
5	○	○	○	○
6	○	○	○	○
7	○	○	○	○
8	○	○	○	○
9	○	○	○	○
10	○	○	○	○
11	○	○	○	○
12	○	○	○	○
13	○	○	○	○
14	○	○	○	○
15	○	○	○	○
16	○	○	○	○
17	○	○	○	○
18	○	○	○	○
19	○	○	○	○
20	○	○	○	○
21	○	○	○	○
22	○	○	○	○
23	○	○	○	○
24	○	○	○	○
25	○	○	○	○

SECTION 2 — 65 marks

Attempt ALL questions

It should be noted that question 11 contains a choice.

1. Recently a new class of RNA, called microRNA, has been discovered. These small RNA molecules have an important role in controlling the translation of mRNA. This type of control is called RNA interference.

    A microRNA is formed from a precursor RNA molecule that folds into a double-stranded "hairpin" structure. The hairpin is then processed to give a shorter molecule by the enzymes "Drosha" and "Dicer". One strand of this short molecule attaches to RISC proteins; the resulting complex binds to target mRNA molecules and prevents translation (Figure 1).

Figure 1: Control of gene expression by RNA interference

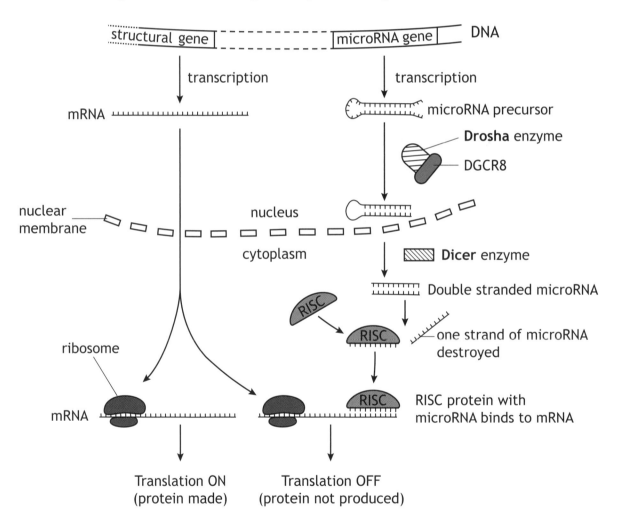

Recent research has investigated the importance of microRNA in controlling the fate of stem cells. Stem cells can either divide rapidly to make more stem cells, a process called **self-renewal**, or differentiate into specialised cell types. To determine the role of microRNAs in these processes, stem cells were modified to "knock out" microRNA production. These microRNA knockout cells lack the protein DGCR8, an activator of Drosha. Figures 2A and 2B compare growth rate and cell-cycle progression in knockout and normal cells.

1. (continued)

In further work, the differentiation of knockout and normal cells was studied by inducing the cells to differentiate. Analysis was carried out on the levels of specific marker molecules whose presence is associated with either self-renewal or differentiation. Results are shown in Figures 3A and 3B.

Figure 2A: Effect of knockout on growth rate

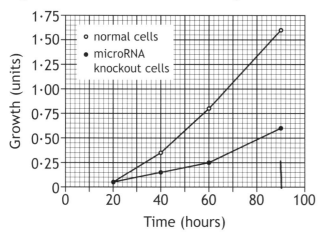

Figure 2B: Effect of knockout on cell cycle

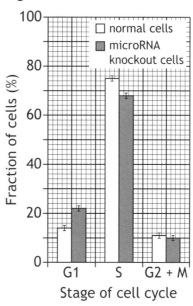

Figure 3A: Level of self-renewal marker

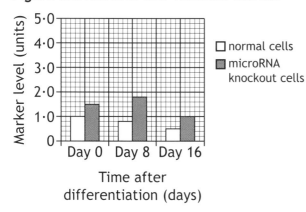

Figure 3B: Level of differentiation marker

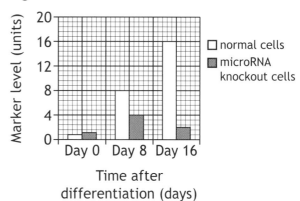

MARKS | DO NOT WRITE IN THIS MARGIN

(a) State the term that describes the entire set of proteins expressed by a genome.

1

(b) Describe the process by which the knockout of DGCR8 affects RNA interference.

2

MARKS | DO NOT WRITE IN THIS MARGIN

1. **(continued)**

(c) (i) Describe what happens during the G1 phase of the cell cycle. 1

(ii) Using Figure 2A, calculate the percentage reduction in growth at 90 hours caused by the microRNA knockout. 1

(iii) The researchers concluded that microRNA knockout cells do not progress normally through the cell cycle.

Explain how the results in Figure 2B support this conclusion. 2

(d) (i) Use Figures 3A and 3B. Give one general conclusion about the expression of the differentiation marker by comparing normal and knockout cells. 1

(ii) There is a hypothesis that self-renewal is switched off as differentiation proceeds and that the interaction of these two processes is abnormal in knockout cells.

Explain how the data support this hypothesis. 2

MARKS | DO NOT WRITE IN THIS MARGIN

2. Gamma-aminobutyric acid (GABA) is a neurotransmitter that functions as a signalling molecule in the central nervous system. GABA binds to a receptor protein located in the plasma membrane of target cells as shown in Figure 1. Binding of a GABA molecule opens a channel that allows chloride ions (Cl^-) to enter the cell.

Figure 1   **Figure 2**

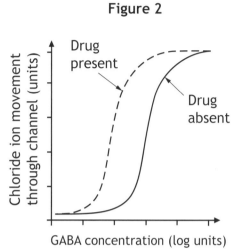

Benzodiazepines are sedative drugs that bind to the receptor protein and increase its affinity for GABA. These drugs act as allosteric modulators by binding at a site that is distinct from the GABA-binding site. Figure 2, above, shows the movement of chloride ions through the channel as GABA is increased with and without the drug being present.

(a) Using the information provided, explain why the GABA receptor is described as a ligand-gated channel.   2

_____

_____

(b) State the term that describes the action of a membrane receptor in which signal binding brings about an effect in the cytoplasm.   1

_____

(c) (i) Describe the information in Figure 2 that shows that the affinity of the receptor for GABA has been increased by the benzodiazepine.   1

_____

_____

MARKS | DO NOT WRITE IN THIS MARGIN

2. (continued)

(ii) Explain why the affinity of the receptor for GABA increases when the drug binds to the modulatory site.

1

_____

_____

(iii) Describe the effect that chloride ion influx will have on the membrane potential of the nerve cell.

1

_____

_____

MARKS | DO NOT WRITE IN THIS MARGIN

3. An investigation into the effects of different concentrations of ATP on muscle tissue used muscle from three pork chops (A, B and C), all bought from the same shop.

Three thin strips of muscle were cut from each chop and placed on microscope slides. The length of each strip was measured and recorded.

Equal volumes of a 10% ATP solution were added to one strip of muscle from each chop and the length of each measured again.

The experiment was repeated using a 5% ATP solution on the second set of strips and distilled water on the final set.

(a) Identify the independent variable in this experiment.   1

_____

(b) Two confounding variables in this experiment are temperatures of the solutions and muscle strips during the experiment, and the breed of pig that the chops came from.

    (i) Suggest one further confounding variable in this experiment.   1

_____

_____

    (ii) Explain the way in which this variable could affect the outcome of this experiment.   1

_____

_____

The following table shows the data collected.

Solution added to strip	Pork chop strip sample	Initial length (mm)	Final length (mm)	Change in length (mm)
10% ATP	A	10	8	2
	B	11	8	3
	C	10	11	1
5% ATP	A	12	11	1
	B	13	12	1
	C	11	10	1
Distilled water	A	12	12	0
	B	12	13	1
	C	9	10	1

MARKS | DO NOT WRITE IN THIS MARGIN

3. (continued)

(c) State whether or not the data is reliable. Explain your answer.   2

_____

_____

_____

(d) Name the type of control used in this experiment.   1

_____

(e) Suggest how selection bias has affected the validity of this experiment.   1

_____

_____

MARKS | DO NOT WRITE IN THIS MARGIN

4. When insulin attaches to its receptor in the plasma membrane of fat cells and muscle cells, GLUT 4 glucose transporter proteins in the cytoplasm are recruited into the membrane to take in glucose. Type 2 diabetes is associated with insulin resistance in which cells are less able to respond to insulin in this way.

A recent study concluded that moderate strength training increases the GLUT 4 content of muscle tissue in those with type 2 diabetes. Individuals taking part all did strength training on one leg (T leg) for six weeks while the other leg was left untrained (UT leg). The subjects either had type 2 diabetes or did not. At the end of the training, muscle biopsies (samples) were taken from the trained and untrained legs and compared for GLUT 4 protein content. The results are shown in the graph below.

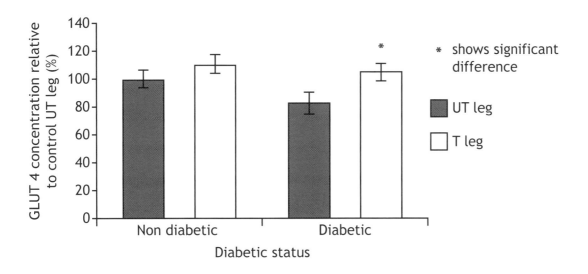

(a) State a suitable null hypothesis in this investigation.   1

_____

_____

(b) The researchers concluded that moderate strength training increases the GLUT 4 content of muscle tissue **only** in those with type 2 diabetes. Identify the evidence that supports this conclusion.   2

_____

_____

_____

(c) State why the treatment regimes for subjects with type 1 diabetes may differ from subjects with type 2 diabetes.   1

_____

_____

5. Thyroxine is a hormone that acts as a regulator of metabolic rate in most tissues. Thyroxine causes an increase in metabolic rate by binding to specific receptors located within the nucleus of a target cell. Hyperthyroidism is a condition caused by overproduction of thyroxine. The following graph shows the average change in metabolic rate of individuals with hyperthyroidism who were treated over a 20-week period with a drug (carbimazole). The drug decreases the synthesis of thyroxine from the thyroid gland.

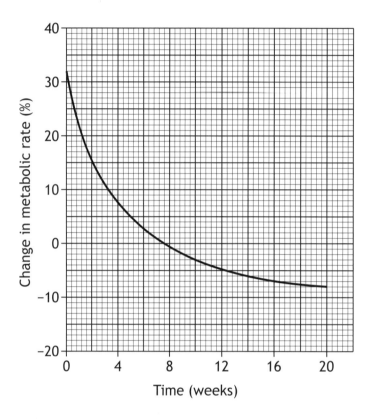

(a) State the property of thyroxine that allows it to cross the membrane of cells.   1

_____

(b) Describe the mechanism by which thyroxine binding to its receptor affects transcription of genes that influence metabolic rate.   2

_____

_____

_____

MARKS | DO NOT WRITE IN THIS MARGIN

5. (continued)

(c)   (i)   Explain how the data support the conclusion that the thyroid gland has large stores of thyroxine.

1

_____

_____

(ii)   Explain why the changes in metabolic rate have been presented as percentages.

1

_____

_____

MARKS | DO NOT WRITE IN THIS MARGIN

6. Rod cells and cone cells are photoreceptors in vertebrate eyes. Membranes in these cells contain rhodopsin, a protein molecule that has a light-absorbing component. Rhodopsin generates a nerve impulse when light is absorbed.

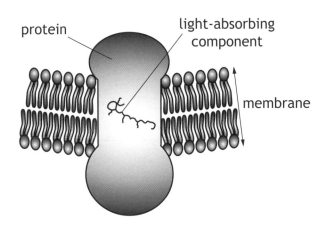

(a) Name the light-absorbing component of rhodopsin.   1

_____

(b) Explain the mechanism by which the absorption of a photon by rhodopsin leads to the generation of a nerve impulse.   2

_____

_____

_____

_____

(c) Give one feature of the photoreceptor system in rods that allows these cells to function in low light intensity.   1

_____

_____

MARKS DO NOT WRITE IN THIS MARGIN

7. A type of haemophilia results when a gene that codes for a blood clotting factor, factor VIII, is mutated. This gene is located on the X chromosome. Mutated alleles do not produce functional factor VIII.

(a) Explain why men are more likely than women to be affected by this type of haemophilia.

2

_____

_____

_____

(b) An unaffected man and a carrier woman have a daughter and a son.

State the probability of each child being able to produce functional factor VIII.

2

Space for calculation and working

Daughter _____

Son _____

(c) (i) Explain the importance of inactivation of the X chromosome in females.

1

_____

_____

(ii) Analysis of a female carrier showed that her blood contained only 42% of the normal levels of functional factor VIII.

Suggest why this value was lower than predicted.

1

_____

_____

MARKS | DO NOT WRITE IN THIS MARGIN

8. Describe how the events that occur during crossing over contribute to the production of variable gametes.

4

_____

_____

_____

_____

_____

_____

9. The following figure shows the life cycle of the macroparasitic flatworm called *Schistosoma japonicum*. The flatworm can live for many years within a host. In humans, if untreated, it causes the disease schistosomiasis (bilharzia) that can be fatal.

Life cycle of *Schistosoma japonicum*

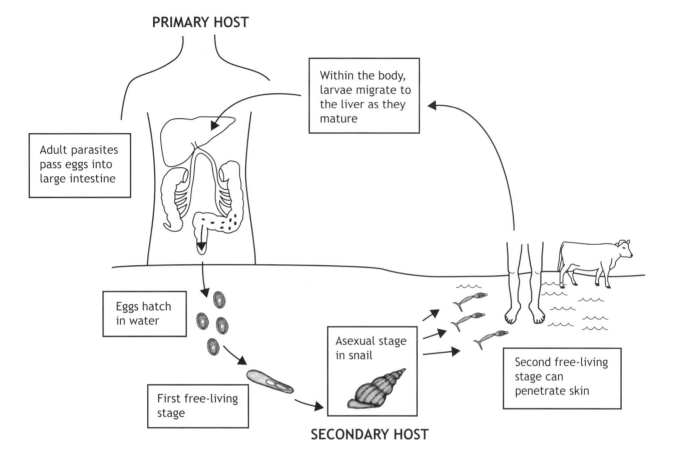

		MARKS	DO NOT WRITE IN THIS MARGIN
(a)	(i) Explain why the snail may **not** be described as a vector.	1	
	(ii) Suggest a feature of this parasite's life cycle that can lead to an increased rate of transmission.	1	

MARKS | DO NOT WRITE IN THIS MARGIN

9. (continued)

(b) Parasites living inside a host will be exposed to attack by the host's immune system.

Describe one way in which parasites may overcome the immune response of their hosts.

1

_____

_____

(c) Describe the Red Queen hypothesis.

2

_____

_____

MARKS | DO NOT WRITE IN THIS MARGIN

10. Fur seals spend most of their lives feeding in Antarctic seas. During the short summer they come ashore to breed.

The figure below shows the number of fur seals breeding on Signy Island from 1956 to 1986.

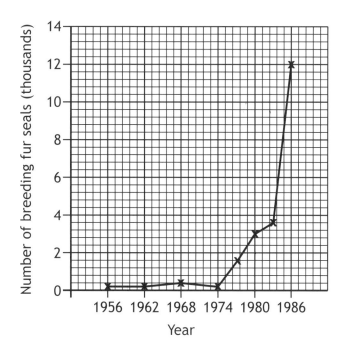

(a) Calculate the percentage increase in the size of the breeding seal population between 1980 and 1986.

1

Space for calculation and working

_____ %

MARKS | DO NOT WRITE IN THIS MARGIN

10. **(continued)**

(b) Permanent quadrats were established to investigate the effect of fur seals on ground cover plants. The table shows the mean percentage of cover of a number of plant species sampled in the permanent quadrats in 1965 and 1985.

Plant species	Percentage cover (%)	
	1965	1985
Drepanocladus uncinatus	30	0
Bryum algens	49	0
Tortula filaris	16	0
Tortula saxicola	4	4
Prasiola crispa	1	41

(i) Explain the changes in percentage cover between 1965 and 1985.   **2**

_____

_____

_____

(ii) Suggest why the percentage cover in 1985 is not 100%.   **1**

_____

_____

(c) (i) Describe one consideration that must be taken into account when carrying out sampling in an ecosystem.   **1**

_____

_____

(ii) Describe the process of stratified sampling.   **1**

_____

_____

MARKS | DO NOT WRITE IN THIS MARGIN

11. Answer **either A or B** in the space below.

A   Describe the specific cellular defences that protect mammals from parasite infection.   8

OR

B   Describe courtship behaviours that affect reproductive success.   8

[END OF SPECIMEN QUESTION PAPER]

MARKS | DO NOT WRITE IN THIS MARGIN

ADDITIONAL SPACE FOR ANSWERS AND ROUGH WORK

MARKS | DO NOT WRITE IN THIS MARGIN

ADDITIONAL SPACE FOR ANSWERS AND ROUGH WORK

[BLANK PAGE]

DO NOT WRITE ON THIS PAGE

ADVANCED HIGHER FOR CfE

Model Paper 1

Whilst this Model Paper has been specially commissioned by Hodder Gibson for use as practice for the Advanced Higher (for Curriculum for Excellence) exams, the key reference document remains the SQA Specimen Paper 2015.

HODDER GIBSON
LEARN MORE

National
Qualifications
MODEL PAPER 1

Biology
Section 1—Questions

Duration — 2 hours 30 minutes

Instructions for the completion of Section 1 are given on *Page two* of your question and answer booklet.

Record your answers on the answer grid on *Page three* of your question and answer booklet.

Before leaving the examination room you must give your question and answer booklet to the Invigilator; if you do not, you may lose all the marks for this paper.

HODDER
GIBSON
LEARN MORE

SECTION 1 — 25 marks

Attempt ALL questions

1. The diagrams below represent the general actions of enzymes involved in the transfer of phosphate groups in cells.

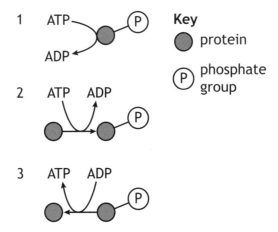

Which line in the table below identifies the enzymes involved in each diagram?

	Phosphatases	ATP-ases	Kinases
A	1	2	3
B	3	1	2
C	2	3	1
D	1	3	2

2. Which line in the table below describes the charges on the two components of nucleosomes?

	Charge on nucleosome component	
	DNA	Histone proteins
A	negative	negative
B	positive	negative
C	positive	positive
D	negative	positive

3. The table below shows the charges on the R groups of four amino acids at a certain pH. An artificial polypeptide consisting of a chain of only 24 of these amino acids has the ratio 3 glycerates : 2 asparates : 2 lysines : 1 glycine and is shown in the diagram below. The charge on each chain terminus is also shown.

Table

Charge on R Group = +1	Charge on R Group = −1
glycerate	lysine
aspartate	glycine

Diagram

Chain of amino acids in an artificial polypeptide

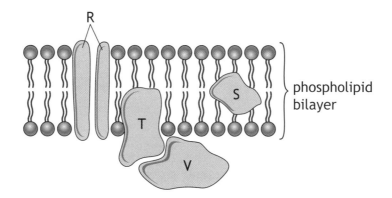

From the information given, what is the overall net charge on this polypeptide at this pH?

A   −6

B   −3

C   +3

D   +6

4. The diagram below shows the arrangement of four protein molecules, R, S, T and V, and the phospholipid bilayer in a fragment of cell membrane.

Which of the protein molecules shown are integral membrane proteins?

A   S only

B   R only

C   R, S and T

D   R, S, T and V

5. The diagram below shows two conformational states of molecules of the Na/K transporter protein in a cell membrane and the release of Na⁺ and K⁺ ions from them.

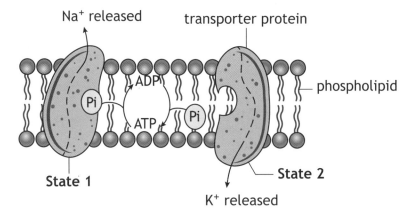

Which line in the table below identifies the affinity for Na⁺ ions of each conformational state of this protein?

	State 1	State 2
A	low	high
B	low	low
C	high	high
D	high	low

6. Common self-heal, *Prunella vulgaris,* is a perennial plant species found in moist grassland habitats at various altitudes throughout Europe.

A transplant experiment was carried out to investigate the contribution of genes and the environment to the stem height of this species. Specimens of young apomictic plants were collected at altitudes of 1000 metres and 2000 metres and transplanted at both altitudes. The heights of the stems of the transplanted individuals were measured after a year and means calculated as shown in the table below.

Altitude from which young plants were collected (m)	Mean height of stems (cm)	
	Plants grown at 1000 m	Plants grown at 2000 m
1000	25 ± 8	19 ± 4
2000	18 ± 4	10 ± 2

Which observations could be used to justify the conclusion that variation in height is determined to some extent by the environment?

A   Plants from different altitudes have similar heights when grown in different environments.

B   Plants from the same altitude have different heights when grown in different environments.

C   Plants from different altitudes have different heights when grown in the same environment.

D   Plants from the same altitude have different heights when grown in the same environment.

7. The diagram below shows a glucose and sodium ion (Na⁺) symport in the membrane of a cell from the lining of the human small intestine.

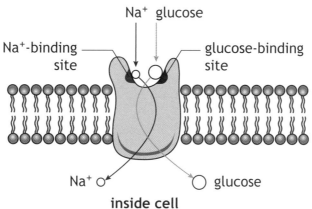

Which line in the table below represents the relative concentrations of glucose and sodium ions (Na⁺) on the two sides of the plasma membrane?

	Sodium ions (Na^+)		Glucose	
	Outside cell	Inside cell	Outside cell	Inside cell
A	high	low	low	high
B	high	low	high	low
C	low	high	low	high
D	low	high	high	low

8. Some stages of muscle contraction are listed below.

1   Phosphate ion released from myosin head

2   ATP binds to myosin head and causes it to detach from actin filament

3   Myosin head swings forward and attaches to actin filament

4   Myosin head drags along actin filament

In which sequence do these stages occur as contraction progresses?

A   2, 1, 3, 4

B   2, 3, 1, 4

C   3, 2, 1, 4

D   3, 2, 4, 1

9. Zidovudine is an anti-viral drug which can be used in the treatment of HIV 1 infections in humans. It inhibits the action of reverse transcriptase during the life cycle of the virus.

   At which stage in the life cycle would zidovudine be most effective?

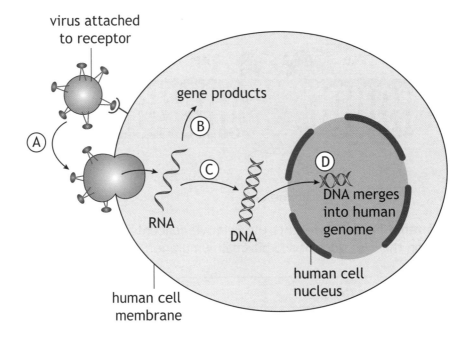

10. Temperature influences the binding and release of oxygen molecules by haemoglobin.

   The graph below shows the percentage oxygen saturation of haemoglobin at three different temperatures: 34°C, 37°C and 42°C.

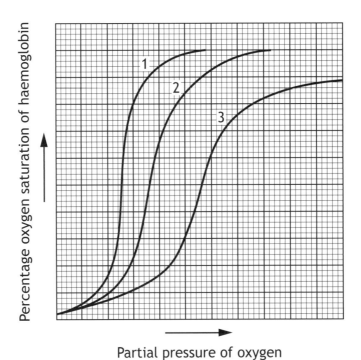

10. **(continued)**

Which line in the table below identifies these temperatures?

	Graph 1	Graph 2	Graph 3
A	34°C	37°C	42°C
B	37°C	42°C	34°C
C	34°C	42°C	37°C
D	42°C	37°C	34°C

11. Which line in the table below describes the steroid hormone thyroxine and its effect on genes that increase metabolic rate?

	Type of signal molecule	Location of receptor molecule binding	Effect on transcription
A	hydrophobic	nucleus	removes inhibition
B	hydrophilic	membrane	inhibits
C	hydrophobic	nucleus	inhibits
D	hydrophilic	membrane	removes inhibition

12. Which of the following situations would be expected to increase the rate of evolution?

A   having a longer generation time

B   living in a cooler environment

C   reducing selection pressure

D   transferring genes horizontally

13. In birds, **females** are heterogametic. The gene for feather-barring in domestic chickens is sex-linked. The allele for barred feathers is dominant to the allele for non-barred feathers.

Which ratio of offspring would be expected if a non-barred male was crossed with a barred female?

A   1 barred female : 1 barred male

B   1 non-barred male : 1 non-barred female

C   1 barred male : 1 non-barred female

D   1 non-barred male : 1 barred female

14. The Lincoln Index N = MC/R is used to estimate the size (N) of certain animal populations during field investigations. A sample of the population is captured and marked (M). After an appropriate time, a second sample is captured (C) and any recaptured individuals are counted (R).

The list below shows possible assumptions and precautions related to the method used.

1. All individuals have an equal chance of being captured.

2. Immigration and emigration occur at equal rates.

3. The sampling methods used are kept the same.

Which items in the list must be **true** for a valid and reliable population estimate?

A   1 only

B   1 and 3 only

C   2 and 3 only

D   1, 2 and 3

15. All viruses consist of a protein coat surrounding

A   DNA or RNA

B   DNA and RNA

C   DNA only

D   RNA only.

16. Which of the following is **not** a source of DNA during horizontal gene transfer in bacteria?

A   gametes

B   viruses

C   plasmids

D   bacterial chromosomes

17. The diagram below shows the life cycle of a parasitic worm that causes schistosomiasis in humans.

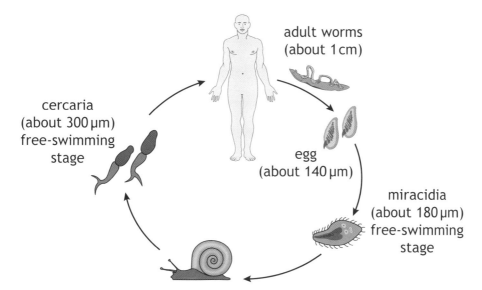

Which line in the table below shows the roles of the various species in the life cycle of this parasite?

	Definitive host	Intermediate host	Vector species involved?
A	snail	human	yes
B	human	snail	yes
C	human	snail	no
D	snail	human	no

18. Which of the following features of a parasite may be considered a part of its extended phenotype?

A   virulence

B   rapid antigen change

C   high genetic variability

D   alteration of host behaviour

19. The parental investment strategy of a species can be classified as K-selected or r-selected.

Which line in the table below describes the characteristics of K-selected species compared to r-selected species?

	K-selected compared to r-selected	
	Number of offspring	Size of offspring produced
A	larger	larger
B	larger	smaller
C	smaller	larger
D	smaller	smaller

20. The red-necked phalarope, *Phalaropus lobatus,* is a ground-nesting wading bird. The females have brighter plumage than the males, and the males carry out much of the egg incubation.

This situation is described as

A   satellite male strategy

B   reversed sexual dimorphism

C   lekking behaviour

D   parthenogenesis.

21. The diagram below shows a response by B-lymphocytes to foreign antigens.

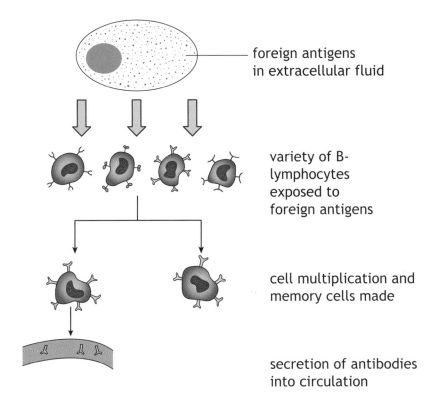

Which of the following identifies this cellular response?

A   apoptosis

B   phagocytosis

C   inflammation

D   clonal selection

22. The graph below shows how the egg-laying rate of three different strains of white leghorn hen varies with their age.

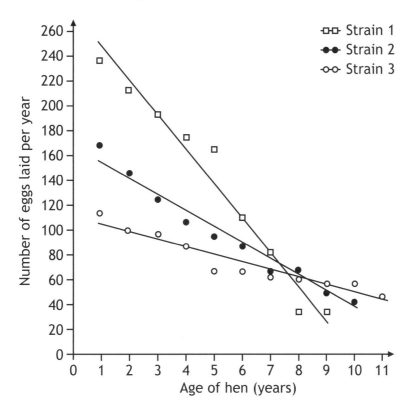

Which of the following conclusions **can** be supported from the information shown?

A   Older hens have a higher egg-laying rate than younger hens.

B   Egg-laying rate decreases faster with age in hens that lay more eggs early in life.

C   The number of eggs laid throughout life is approximately equal in all three strains.

D   Egg-laying rate in later life is independent of egg-laying rate in earlier years.

23. Eggs of leopard geckos kept in breeding cages were collected and incubated at two temperatures over five breeding seasons. When each new gecko hatched, its gender was noted. The graph below shows how gender in the gecko population varied at each temperature.

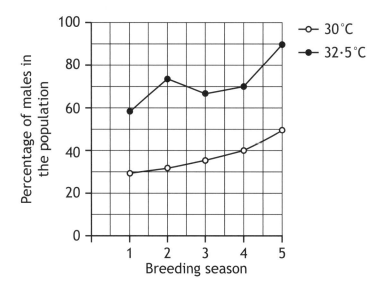

How many females would be present in a population of 500 geckos after four seasons at 32·5°C?

A   150

B   200

C   300

D   350

24. The diagram below represents the distribution of two species of barnacle on a rocky shore. The fundamental and realised niches of the two species are shown by the vertical lines W, X, Y and Z.

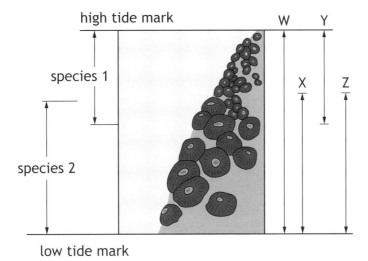

The realised niche of species 2 is shown by line Z.

Which line in the table below identifies the other niches illustrated?

	Fundamental niche of species 1	Fundamental niche of species 2	Realised niche of species 1
A	W	Y	X
B	Y	X	W
C	W	X	Y
D	X	W	Y

25. In terms of selection, fitness can be describes as absolute or relative.

Absolute fitness is the ratio of

A surviving offspring of one phenotype compared to other phenotypes

B frequencies of a particular genotype in one generation compared to the next

C surviving offspring of one genotype compared to other genotypes

D frequencies of a particular phenotype in one generation compared to the next.

[END OF SECTION 1. NOW ATTEMPT THE QUESTIONS IN SECTION 2 OF YOUR QUESTION AND ANSWER BOOKLET]

AH

National
Qualifications
MODEL PAPER 1

Mark

Biology
Section 1 — Answer Grid and Section 2

Duration — 2 hours 30 minutes

Fill in these boxes and read what is printed below.

Full name of centre

Town

Forename(s)

Surname

Number of seat

Date of birth

Day	Month	Year	Scottish candidate number

Total marks — 90

SECTION 1 — 25 marks

Attempt ALL questions.

Instructions for completion of Section 1 are given on *Page two*.

SECTION 2 — 65 marks

Attempt ALL questions.

Write your answers clearly in the spaces provided in this booklet. Additional space for answers and rough work is provided at the end of this booklet. If you use this space you must clearly identify the question number you are attempting. Any rough work must be written in this booklet. You should score through your rough work when you have written your final copy.

Use **blue** or **black** ink.

Before leaving the examination room you must give this booklet to the Invigilator; if you do not you may lose all the marks for this paper.

SECTION 1— 25 marks

The questions for Section 1 are contained on *Page 45*—Questions.
Read these and record your answers on the answer grid on *Page 63* opposite.
Use **blue** or **black** ink. Do NOT use gel pens or pencil.

1.   The answer to each question is **either** A, B, C or D. Decide what your answer is, then fill in the appropriate bubble (see sample question below).

2.   There is **only one correct** answer to each question.

3.   Any rough working should be done on the additional space for answers and rough work at the end of this booklct.

Sample Question

The thigh bone is called the

    A   humerus

    B   femur

    C   tibia

    D   fibula.

The correct answer is **B**—femur. The answer **B** bubble has been clearly filled in (see below).

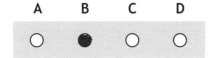

Changing an answer

If you decide to change your answer, cancel your first answer by putting a cross through it (see below) and fill in the answer you want. The answer below has been changed to **D**.

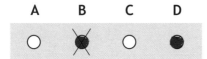

If you then decide to change back to an answer you have already scored out, put a tick (✓) to the **right** of the answer you want, as shown below:

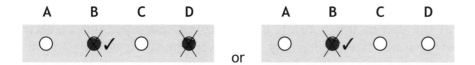

SECTION 1 — Answer Grid

	A	B	C	D
1	○	○	○	○
2	○	○	○	○
3	○	○	○	○
4	○	○	○	○
5	○	○	○	○
6	○	○	○	○
7	○	○	○	○
8	○	○	○	○
9	○	○	○	○
10	○	○	○	○
11	○	○	○	○
12	○	○	○	○
13	○	○	○	○
14	○	○	○	○
15	○	○	○	○
16	○	○	○	○
17	○	○	○	○
18	○	○	○	○
19	○	○	○	○
20	○	○	○	○
21	○	○	○	○
22	○	○	○	○
23	○	○	○	○
24	○	○	○	○
25	○	○	○	○

SECTION 2 — 65 marks

Attempt ALL questions

It should be noted that question 11 contains a choice.

1. Aquaporin 1 (AQP1) is a membrane protein which channels the movement of water molecules. AQP1 has four sub-units, each of which acts as a water channel, as shown in **Figure 1** below.

Figure 1: A fragment of membrane containing AQP1

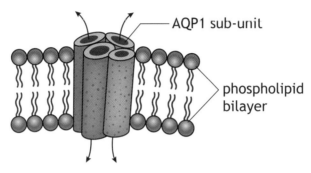

AQP1 sub-unit

phospholipid bilayer

⟶ = water movement

Red blood cells were prepared by allowing them to take up water molecules labelled with a radioactive isotope of hydrogen. The membranes of some of these prepared cells were then phosphorylated to deactivate their membrane AQP1s. Some were left untreated.

Treated and untreated cells were bathed in isotonic and hypertonic solutions and the average rates of water movement through their membranes were measured. The results are shown in **Table 1** below.

Table 1: Rate of water movement across membranes

Bathing solution	Average rate of water movement through membranes (units)	
	Cells with active AQP1	Cells with deactivated AQP1
Isotonic with cell contents	3·5	1·4
Hypertonic to cell contents	28·0	2·2

1. **(continued)**

   Figure 2 represents part of a kidney tubule from a mouse. Cells with AQP1 are found in the walls of this part of the tubule and the blood capillaries associated with it. About 70% of water in the fluid entering the tubule is reabsorbed into the blood as it passes through this region. Water which is not reabsorbed passes through the tubule and appears in the urine.

   Figure 2: Representation of part of a kidney tubule from a mouse

   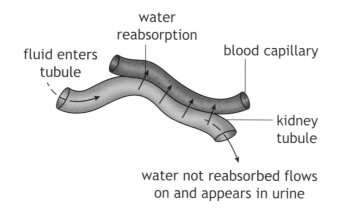

   Presence of aquaporins in the kidney tubule cells is determined by the allele **N**. Mice with genotype **nn** have no aquaporins in their kidney tubule cells. In a study of the importance of aquaporins in the kidney function, mice of different genotypes were selected as shown.

Group 1	genotype	**NN**	aquaporins present
Group 2	genotype	**Nn**	heterozygous
Group 3	genotype	**nn**	aquaporins absent

   Average body masses of the mice and the average solute concentration of their urine were measured before and after a period without water. The results are shown in **Figure 3** and **Figure 4** below.

Figure 3: % change in average body mass over a period without water

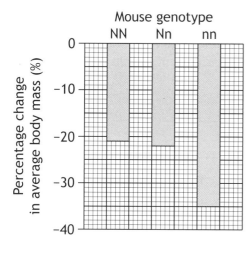

Figure 4: Urine solute concentration before and after a period without water

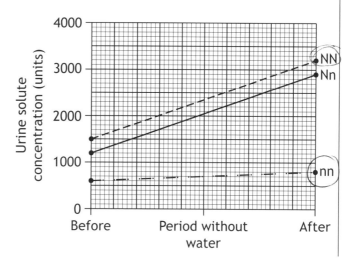

MARKS | DO NOT WRITE IN THIS MARGIN

1. **(continued)**

(a) (i) Give the term used for proteins such as AQP1 which are embedded into a phospholipid membrane, as shown in **Figure 1**.   1

_____

(ii) With reference to AQP1, describe what is meant by the quaternary structure of a protein.   1

_____

_____

(b) Explain why water labelled with radioactive hydrogen was used in this experiment.   1

_____

(c) (i) Use data in **Table 1** to draw conclusions about:

1 how activating AQP1 affects water flow across membranes;   1

_____

_____

2 how the water concentration gradient, as well as the activity of AQP1, affects the rate of water flow across membranes.   1

_____

_____

(ii) Predict the effect of osmosis on the average masses of the cells after immersion in the isotonic solution.   1

_____

_____

(d) (i) Using information from **Figure 4**, explain the percentage of body mass lost by mice in Group 3 compared with those in Group 1 shown in Figure 3.   2

_____

_____

(ii) Use the data in **Figures 3 and 4** to show that the heterozygous mice in Group 2 have enough AQP1 to make them capable of maintaining a steady water concentration in their blood.   2

_____

_____

MARKS | DO NOT WRITE IN THIS MARGIN

2. In a procedure to purify an enzyme, a tissue sample was taken through a number of stages.

The table below describes the purification stages and shows the total mass of protein present and the enzyme activity in the sample following each stage in the purification procedure.

Stage	Description of purification stage	Total protein (mg)	Enzyme activity (units)
1	Liquidise tissue sample	10 000	2 000 000
2	Precipitation by salts	3 000	1 500 000
3	Separation by iso-electric point	500	500 000
4	Affinity chromatography	30	42 000

(a) (i) Calculate the percentage of the protein which had been removed from the liquidised tissue by the end of Stage 4.   **1**

Space for calculation

_____ %

(ii) Enzyme purity in a sample can be calculated using the formula below.

$$enzyme\ purity = \frac{enzyme\ activity}{total\ protein}$$

Use the formula to calculate the number of times by which enzyme purity had been increased between the liquidised sample and the end of Stage 4.   **1**

Space for calculation

_____ times

(b) Explain how separation by iso-electric point, as in Stage 2, occurs.   **2**

_____

_____

_____

(c) In affinity chromatography at Stage 4, a ligand specific to the enzyme being purified was bonded to agarose beads packed into a column.

Describe how this method can improve the purity of the enzyme.   **2**

_____

_____

_____

MARKS | DO NOT WRITE IN THIS MARGIN

3. The diagram below represents part of a molecule of bacteriorhodopsin, a protein found in *Archaea*.

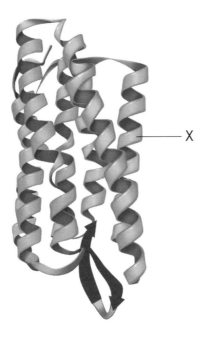

(a) The ribbons in the diagram represent the primary and secondary structures of the protein.

    (i) Describe what is meant by the primary structure of a protein.

    1

_____

_____

    (ii) Name the secondary structural feature shown at X in the diagram and describe how this feature is formed from the primary structure of the protein.

    2

_____

_____

_____

(b) Describe how bacteriorhodopsin generates a potential difference across membranes.

    2

_____

_____

_____

MARKS
DO NOT WRITE IN THIS MARGIN

4. Rod cells and cone cells are photoreceptors in the retinas of vertebrate eyes which are sensitive to photons of light. The diagram below shows a rod cell containing membranes rich in a retinal-opsin complex.

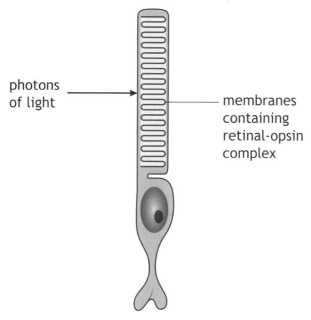

photons of light

membranes containing retinal-opsin complex

(a) Name the retinal-opsin complex found in vertebrate rod cells.

1

(b) The retinal opsin complex activates hundreds of G-protein molecules and so provides amplification in the system.

(i) Describe the role of activated G-protein molecules.

1

(ii) State why amplification is an advantage to vertebrates.

1

(c) Describe how the photoreceptor proteins of cone cells differ from those of rod cells.

1

(d) Explain why the variety of photoreceptor proteins in cone cells provides an advantage to vertebrates.

1

MARKS | DO NOT WRITE IN THIS MARGIN

5. Insulin is a peptide hormone involved in the regulation of blood glucose in humans.

(a) Describe how insulin is involved in the uptake of glucose into target cells.   **2**

_____

_____

_____

(b) (i) Adiponectin is a signalling molecule thought to increase the sensitivity of cells to insulin.

In a clinical study, the concentration of adiponectin in the blood of patients with Type 2 diabetes was compared to non-diabetics. The results are shown in **Table 1** below.

Table 1

Patient Group	Average concentration of adiponectin in blood plasma ($\mu g\,cm^{-3}$)
Type 2 diabetic	$6 \cdot 6 \pm 0 \cdot 4$
Non-diabetic	$7 \cdot 9 \pm 0 \cdot 5$

Explain how the results in **Table 1** relate to the characteristics of Type 2 diabetes.   **2**

_____

_____

_____

MARKS | DO NOT WRITE IN THIS MARGIN

5. (b) (continued)

(ii) **Table 2** below shows results of another clinical study in which increases in adiponectin concentration were determined in individuals at risk of developing Type 2 diabetes who received treatment.

Table 2

Treatment	Average increase in concentration of adiponectin in blood plasma ($\mu g\,cm^{-3}$)
Drug treatment	0.83 ± 0.05
Lifestyle changes	0.23 ± 0.05
Control (no treatment)	0.10 ± 0.05

Compare the results of drug treatment to lifestyle changes in terms of their effectiveness in increasing adiponectin concentration.   1

(iii) Both studies used human volunteers.

1 Give **one** ethical issue which should be considered when using human volunteers.   1

2 Explain why large numbers of volunteers are required to produce reliable results upon which valid conclusions may be based.   1

6. Describe the role of genetic drift in the evolution of new species.

4

_____

_____

_____

_____

_____

_____

7. Feather mites of the order *Sarcoptiformes* (**Figure 1**) are parasites of many birds. The mites feed on oil produced by the birds' oil glands. Oil is applied to feathers during preening times in the mornings and evenings and empties the oil gland. Birds unable to oil their feathers efficiently use more energy maintaining body temperature.

A field investigation into the relationship between mite infection and the breeding success of crested tits (*Parus cristatus*) (**Figure 2**), a species given special protection in Scotland, was carried out.

Figure 1: Feather mite   **Figure 2: Crested tit**

Crested tit nests were located using a systematic search method at a woodland study site and a number of those located were sampled at random. The parent birds from the sample were caught and the following measurements made:

- number of feather mites present
- size of the oil gland.

The nests were monitored and the following data collected:

- number of eggs laid
- number of chicks hatched
- number of chicks which survived to leave the nest.

The breeding success rate was calculated as the percentage of eggs laid from which chicks survived to leave the nest.

The results are shown in the table and graph below.

Table

Number of feather mites on parent birds	Breeding success rate (%)
0	86
2	100
5	64
10	82
14	70
15	85
170	42

Graph

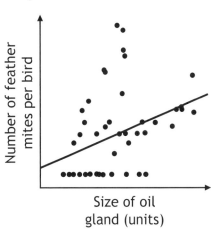

MARKS | DO NOT WRITE IN THIS MARGIN

7. **(continued)**

(a) Suggest the reasons for the following:

(i) a systematic search was carried out to locate the crested tit nests;   1

(ii) a random sample of the nests located was used in the study.   1

(b) Give a null hypothesis appropriate to the investigation.   1

(c) How does the data support the conclusion that feather mite infections reduce breeding success in crested tits?   1

(d) (i) Describe the relationship between size of oil gland and number of feather mites per bird.   1

(ii) Suggest **one** precaution which should be taken to ensure that the oil gland measurements could be validly compared.   1

(e) Identify **one** precaution the investigators should take when working with protected species during their breeding cycle.   1

8. The songs produced by male fruit flies of the genus *Drosophila* are important courtship stimuli. Song is produced by repeated groups of rapid wing vibrations which form distinctive patterns.

The graphs below represent the recorded courtship songs of two closely related species, *Drosophila persimilis* and *Drosophila pseudoobscura*. The two species have similar distributions in western North America.

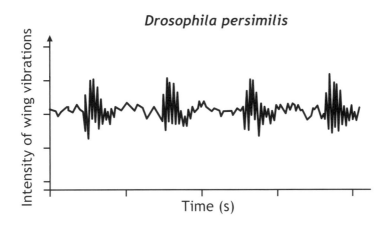

Drosophila persimilis

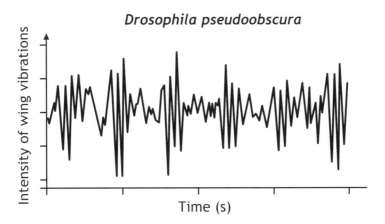

Drosophila pseudoobscura

(a) Compare the intensities and frequencies of the wing vibrations of the two species.

1

_____

_____

MARKS | DO NOT WRITE IN THIS MARGIN

8. **(continued)**

(b) Females of each species discriminate against males which are not of their own species, but males of each species will court females of either species.

(i) Explain the importance of courtship songs to **female** *Drosophila* in terms of the theory of sexual investment.

1

_____

_____

(ii) Explain how the courtship songs of **male** *Drosophila* may have evolved in terms of sexual selection.

2

_____

_____

_____

MARKS | DO NOT WRITE IN THIS MARGIN

9. Female parasitic wasps, *Nasonia vitripennis*, lay their eggs inside the pupae of houseflies, *Musca domestica*. The wasp eggs hatch into larvae that consume the housefly pupae, as shown in the diagram below.

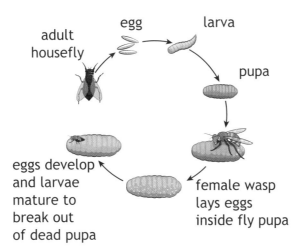

In a study to investigate the evolutionary response of the host to the parasite, two containers were set up with housefly populations. **Container A** had a housefly population with no previous exposure to the parasite and **Container B** had a housefly population which had been exposed to wasp parasitism for a period of three years prior to the study.

The graphs below show how the populations of each species in the containers changed over a 40-week period.

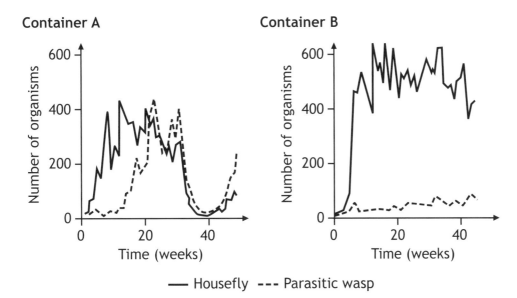

MARKS | DO NOT WRITE IN THIS MARGIN

9. (continued)

(a) (i) Describe how the results support the general conclusion that housefly populations can develop resistance to wasp parasitism.   **1**

_____

_____

(ii) Explain how resistance to wasp parasites may have evolved.   **2**

_____

_____

_____

(b) The response of the houseflies is an example of co-evolution.

(i) Define the term co-evolution.   **1**

_____

_____

(ii) Using the Red Queen hypothesis, predict the population changes in **Container B** if it were left undisturbed over a further period of time.   **1**

_____

_____

_____

MARKS | DO NOT WRITE IN THIS MARGIN

10. A study was planned which aimed to estimate the number of species of mosses and liverworts in a damp woodland area in northern Scotland. As a pilot to the study, preliminary sampling was carried out using different numbers of randomly placed quadrats and the results are shown on the graph below.

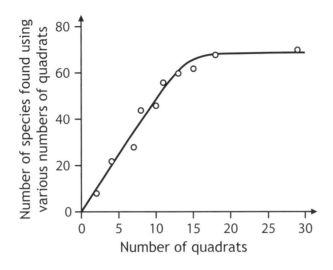

(a) Use information from the graph to explain why each of the following numbers of quadrat would **not** be appropriate for the main survey.

   (i) 10 quadrats   1

   _____

   _____

   (ii) 25 quadrats   1

   _____

   _____

(b) Mosses and liverworts are bryophytes.

   Give **two** other major divisions used to classify the plant kingdom.   2

   _____

   _____

MARKS
DO NOT WRITE IN THIS MARGIN

11. Answer **either A or B** in the space below.

    A   Describe the events of meiosis and how they lead to variation in gametes.   **8**

    OR

    B   Describe the basis of sex determination and how the sex of an organism might change during life.   **8**

Space for answer

[END OF MODEL PAPER]

ADDITIONAL SPACE FOR ANSWERS AND ROUGH WORK

MARKS | DO NOT WRITE IN THIS MARGIN

ADDITIONAL SPACE FOR ANSWERS AND ROUGH WORK

Model Paper 2

Whilst this Model Paper has been specially commissioned by Hodder Gibson for use as practice for the Advanced Higher (for Curriculum for Excellence) exams, the key reference document remains the SQA Specimen Paper 2015.

National
Qualifications
MODEL PAPER 2

Biology
Section 1—Questions

Duration — 2 hours 30 minutes

Instructions for the completion of Section 1 are given on *Page two* of your question and answer booklet.

Record your answers on the answer grid on *Page three* of your question and answer booklet.

Before leaving the examination room you must give your question and answer booklet to the Invigilator; if you do not, you may lose all the marks for this paper.

HODDER
GIBSON
LEARN MORE

SECTION 1 — 25 marks

Attempt ALL questions

1. Immobilised metal ion affinity chromatography (IMAC) can be used to purify proteins. This technique works by allowing proteins with an affinity for metal ions to be retained in a column containing immobilised metal ions, such as cobalt.

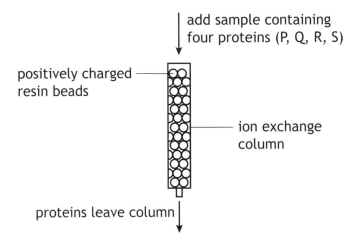

The more negatively charged the protein, the longer it takes to pass through the column.

The graph below shows the time taken for the four proteins to leave the column.

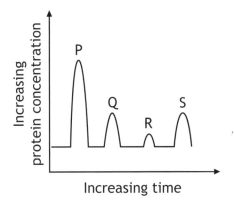

Which conclusion can be drawn from this experiment?

A   Protein P is more negatively charged than protein R.

B   Protein S is more negatively charged than protein Q.

C   Protein R is less negatively charged than protein Q.

D   Protein S is less negatively charged than protein R.

2. The enzyme Na/KATPase moves ions across membranes in the ratio 3 sodium : 2 potassium. 5000 of these ions are pumped across a membrane every 10 seconds.

The number of potassium ions moved across this membrane in one second is

A   200

B   500

C   2000

D   3000.

3. The diagram below represents a plastic well from an immunoassay kit, testing a blood sample from a person who had been exposed to a particular virus. The substrate has been broken down to form a coloured product, so the result is positive.

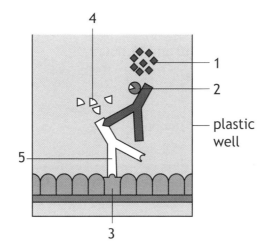

Which line in the table below identifies the numbered components in the well?

	Antigen	Antibody	Reporter enzyme	Substrate
A	3	5	2	4
B	4	1	2	5
C	3	5	4	1
D	5	2	1	4

4. Which of the following diagrams represents the sequence of phases in the cell cycle?

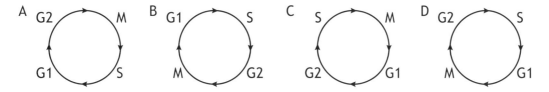

5. The diagram below shows the changes in cell mass and DNA mass during two cell cycles.

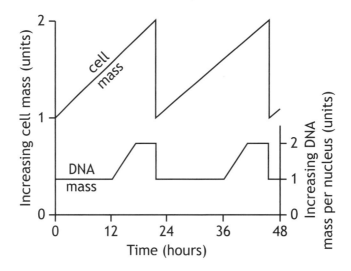

Which valid conclusion could be drawn from the graph?

During the cell cycle

A   replication takes place between 10 and 12 hours

B   mitosis is divided into four phases

C   interphase is the longest phase

D   cytokinesis takes place at 12 and 36 hours.

6. Which of the following techniques can be used to estimate the total cell count?

A   immunoassay

B   haemocytometry

C   chromatography

D   electrophoresis

7. Retinoblastoma protein (Rb) has a role in the regulation of progress through the cell cycle. It can be phosphorylated (Rb-P) or not phosphorylated (Rb).

Which line in the table below shows the phase in the cell cycle during which Rb functions as a regulator and which of its phosphorylation states allows the cell cycle to progress?

	Phase	Phosphorylation state which allows the cycle to progress
A	G1	phosphorylated
B	G1	not phosphorylated
C	S	phosphorylated
D	S	not phosphorylated

8. Which line in the table below identifies factors which trigger apoptosis?

	p53 protein	Cell growth factors
A	present	absent
B	present	present
C	absent	absent
D	absent	present

9. Colorimetry was used to produce the standard curve for soluble protein concentration shown below.

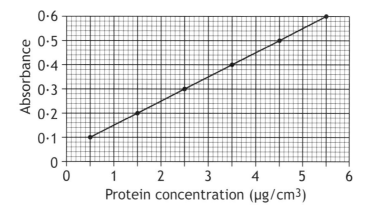

In an experiment to find the soluble protein content of potato tubers, 25g of fresh potato tissue was ground with 50 cm³ of buffer and centrifuged. A total of 65 cm³ of extract was produced.

1 cm³ of the extract was tested in a colorimeter and gave an absorbance of 0·5.

What was the total soluble protein content of the fresh potato tissue in μg per g?

A   3·9

B   9·0

C   11·7

D   13·5

10. The sodium—potassium pump's mechanism of action involves the stages shown below.

P   membrane protein is phosphorylated

Q   sodium ions bind to membrane protein

R   sodium ions are released

S   membrane protein changes conformation

The correct sequence of stages in the action of the pump is

A   P, Q, R, S

B   Q, P, S, R

C   Q, P, R, S

D   P, Q, S, R.

Page five

11. The diagram below shows a structure from a eukaryotic cell about to undergo cell division.

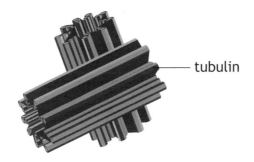

tubulin

Which line in the table below shows the name of the structure and the protein group to which tubulin belongs?

	Name of structure	Protein group
A	cytoskeleton	globular
B	cytoskeleton	integral
C	centrosome	integral
D	centrosome	globular

12. Which line in the table below represents the binding site and effect on affinity of an allosteric enzyme binding with a positive modulator?

	Modulator binding site		Affinity of enzyme for substrate	
	Active site	Secondary site	Increased	Decreased
A				
B				
C				
D				

13. The list below contains terms which refer to signalling molecules.

1   hydrophobic

2   hydrophilic

3   steroid

4   peptide

Which of the terms describe the hormone insulin?

A   1 and 3 only

B   1 and 4 only

C   2 and 3 only

D   2 and 4 only

14. Cortisol is a steroid hormone.

Which letter in the diagram below shows movement by molecules of this hormone in the first stage of its cell signalling process?

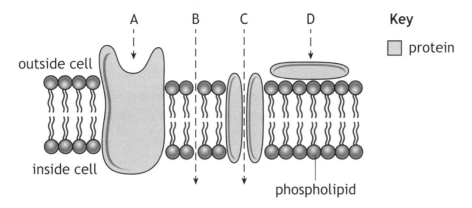

15. The fundamental niche of a species

    A   includes the set of resources available in the absence of competition

    B   includes the set of resources available in the presence of competition

    C   permits co-existence in a community

    D   permits the sharing of resources with other species.

16. The regions of the graph below indicate conditions in four habitats.

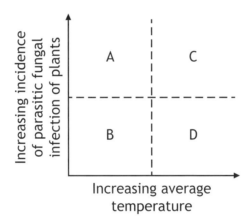

In which habitat is parthenogenesis most likely to evolve as a successful reproductive strategy?

17. Crossing over that generates new allele combinations during meiosis occurs between

    A   sister chromatids of homologous chromosomes

    B   non-sister chromatids of homologous chromosomes

    C   sister chromatids of non-homologous chromosomes

    D   non-sister chromatids of non-homologous chromosomes.

18. A quadrat with sides 50 cm long was used to estimate the densities of the barnacle *Balanus balanoides* in two areas, X and Y, on a rocky shore. Five random samples were taken in each of the two areas and the results are given in the table below.

Quadrat number	Number of individual barnacles	
	Area X	Area Y
1	270	150
2	190	160
3	390	420
4	190	310
5	110	160

Which line in the table below shows the mean density per square metre in the two areas?

	Area X	Area Y
A	230	150
B	460	480
C	920	960
D	1 150	1 200

19. Independent assortment of chromosomes during meiosis results in the production of gametes with varied combinations of chromosomes.

    How many different combinations of chromosomes are possible in the gametes of an organism with a haploid number of 3?

    A   4

    B   6

    C   8

    D   12

20. *Dicrocoelium dendriticum* is a flatworm parasite of grazing animals, such as sheep and cattle.

   Which line in the table shows the phyla to which these species belong?

	Dicrocoelium	*Cattle and sheep*
A	nematoda	chordata
B	platyhelminthes	arthropoda
C	nematoda	arthropoda
D	platyhelminthes	chordata

21. The beef tapeworm *Taenia saginata* is a parasite which does not have a digestive system during part of its life cycle.

   For this reason, the parasite is described as

   A   degenerate

   B   being an ectoparasite

   C   occupying its fundamental niche

   D   co-existing by resource partitioning.

22. The virulence of an infectious organism is defined as the case fatality risk (CFR). CFR can be defined as the percentage of infections which result in death. The table below shows the numbers of people infected by "bird flu" virus (H5N1) in an area and the numbers who died from it over a five year period.

Year	2004	2005	2006	2007	2008
Total infections of H5N1	46	98	115	88	44
Total number of deaths from H5N1 infections	32	43	79	59	33

   In which year was H5N1 most virulent in this area?

   A   2004

   B   2006

   C   2007

   D   2008

23. Measles vaccinations are given to as many children as possible in Scotland. This helps to prevent the spread of measles and gives some protection to non-vaccinated and vulnerable children.

    The protection of non-vaccinated, vulnerable children in this instance is an example of

    A   herd immunity   B   epidemiology

    C   immune surveillance   D   immunological memory.

24. The diagram below shows part of the infection cycle of a human T-cell by an HIV retrovirus.

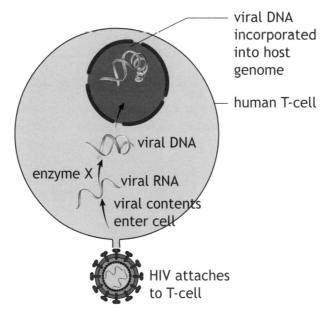

    Enzyme X is

    A   DNAase

    B   DNA polymerase

    C   RNA polymerase

    D   reverse transcriptase.

25. The information in the table below explains terms used in biological science investigations.

    Which line in the table is **not** correct?

	Term	Explanation
A	pilot study	guides modification of experimental design
B	hypothesis	proposes an association between the independent and dependent variable
C	confidence interval	indicates the variability of the data around a mean
D	positive control	provides results in the absence of the treatment

[END OF SECTION 1. NOW ATTEMPT THE QUESTIONS IN SECTION 2 OF YOUR QUESTION AND ANSWER BOOKLET]

AH

National Qualifications
MODEL PAPER 2

Mark

Biology
Section 1 — Answer Grid
and Section 2

Duration — 2 hours 30 minutes

Fill in these boxes and read what is printed below.

Full name of centre

Town

Forename(s)

Surname

Number of seat

Date of birth

Day   Month   Year   Scottish candidate number

Total marks — 90

SECTION 1 — 25 marks

Attempt ALL questions.

Instructions for completion of Section 1 are given on *Page two*.

SECTION 2 — 65 marks

Attempt ALL questions.

Write your answers clearly in the spaces provided in this booklet. Additional space for answers and rough work is provided at the end of this booklet. If you use this space you must clearly identify the question number you are attempting. Any rough work must be written in this booklet. You should score through your rough work when you have written your final copy.

Use **blue** or **black** ink.

Before leaving the examination room you must give this booklet to the Invigilator; if you do not you may lose all the marks for this paper.

SECTION 1— 25 marks

The questions for Section 1 are contained on *Page 83*—Questions.
Read these and record your answers on the answer grid on *Page 97* opposite.
Use **blue** or **black** ink. Do NOT use gel pens or pencil.

1. The answer to each question is **either** A, B, C or D. Decide what your answer is, then fill in the appropriate bubble (see sample question below).

2. There is **only one correct** answer to each question.

3. Any rough working should be done on the additional space for answers and rough work at the end of this booklet.

Sample Question

The thigh bone is called the

    A   humerus

    B   femur

    C   tibia

    D   fibula.

The correct answer is **B**—femur. The answer **B** bubble has been clearly filled in (see below).

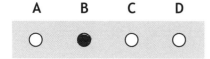

Changing an answer

If you decide to change your answer, cancel your first answer by putting a cross through it (see below) and fill in the answer you want. The answer below has been changed to **D**.

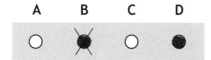

If you then decide to change back to an answer you have already scored out, put a tick (✓) to the **right** of the answer you want, as shown below:

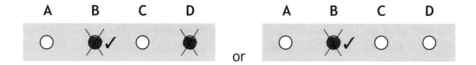

SECTION 1 — Answer Grid

	A	B	C	D
1	○	○	○	○
2	○	○	○	○
3	○	○	○	○
4	○	○	○	○
5	○	○	○	○
6	○	○	○	○
7	○	○	○	○
8	○	○	○	○
9	○	○	○	○
10	○	○	○	○
11	○	○	○	○
12	○	○	○	○
13	○	○	○	○
14	○	○	○	○
15	○	○	○	○
16	○	○	○	○
17	○	○	○	○
18	○	○	○	○
19	○	○	○	○
20	○	○	○	○
21	○	○	○	○
22	○	○	○	○
23	○	○	○	○
24	○	○	○	○
25	○	○	○	○

SECTION 2 — 65 marks

Attempt ALL questions

It should be noted that question 11 contains a choice.

1. Muscle tissue contains both red and white muscle cell types. Glucose is transported into these cells through trans-membrane proteins called glucose transporters (GLUTs).

   GLUT1 is responsible for glucose uptake in all cells. The membranes of muscle cells also contain GLUT4.

   An investigation was carried out into how the two different GLUTs contributed to glucose uptake by the two different types of muscle cell before and after exposure to insulin. The results are shown in **Figure 1**.

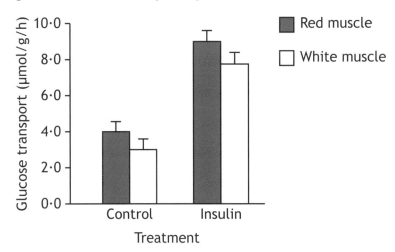

Figure 1: Glucose transport by cells with and without insulin

Membranes from muscle cells were isolated and centrifuged to separate the plasma membranes (PM) from internal membranes (IM). The protein components of the membranes were separated by gel electrophoresis and then blotted. The resulting blots were exposed to radioactively labelled antibodies specific to each of the two GLUT proteins to allow identification and quantification. **Figure 2** shows the effects of exposure to insulin on the GLUT levels in each type of muscle.

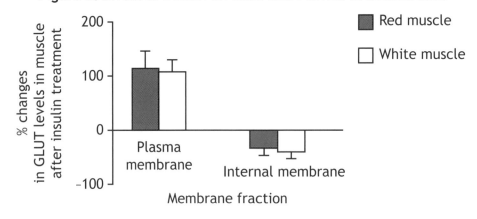

Figure 2: Effect of insulin on total GLUT levels in muscle cells

MARKS | DO NOT WRITE IN THIS MARGIN

1. **(continued)**

In **Figure 3** the size and darkness of the blots indicates the levels of the two GLUTs in the membranes of red and white muscle cells.

Figure 3

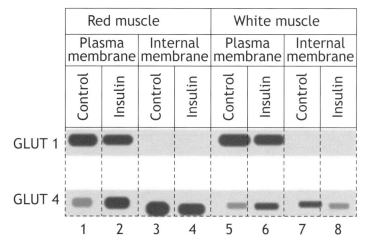

(a) Use data from **Figure 1** to support the statement that red muscle cells have a greater capacity for glucose transport than white muscle cells.   2

_____

_____

_____

(b) From the results shown in **Figure 2**, it was concluded that both muscle types have the same underlying GLUT level response to insulin.

Explain how the bars of standard error support this conclusion.   1

_____

_____

(c) Using data from **Figure 3**:

   (i) describe the distribution of GLUT1 in muscle cells before insulin treatment;   1

_____

_____

   (ii) give one conclusion about the effect of insulin treatment on GLUT1;   1

_____

   (iii) give evidence that the effect of insulin on GLUT4 is the same in both types of muscle cell.   1

_____

_____

MARKS

1. **(continued)**

(d) A hypothesis was proposed which suggested that insulin triggers the transport of GLUT4 to the plasma membrane from the internal membranes and that more of this transport occurs in red muscle cells compared with white.

Outline the support for this hypothesis that can be seen in **Figure 3**.   2

_____

_____

_____

(e) Suggest an explanation for the reduced uptake of glucose by cells, which is characteristic of type 2 diabetes.   2

_____

_____

_____

MARKS | DO NOT WRITE IN THIS MARGIN

2. The diagram below shows events which occur in part of the thylakoid membrane of a chloroplast from a green plant after a photon of light strikes a chlorophyll molecule.

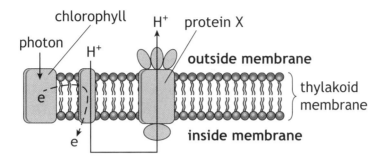

(a) Describe the mechanisms by which:

   (i) absorption of a photon by chlorophyll results in the movement of H⁺ ions to the inside of the thylakoid membrane;   2

   _____

   _____

   _____

   (ii) the H⁺ ions return through the thylakoid membrane to the outside.   1

   _____

   _____

(b) Name protein **X** through which the H⁺ ions pass and explain the advantage of its action to the plant.   2

   _____

   _____

   _____

MARKS | DO NOT WRITE IN THIS MARGIN

3. The phospholipid layer in membranes acts as a barrier to some molecules, although others can pass through. Transmembrane proteins can act as channels or transporters to perform specific functions.

The diagram shows three transmembrane proteins, X, Y and Z, in a phospholipid membrane.

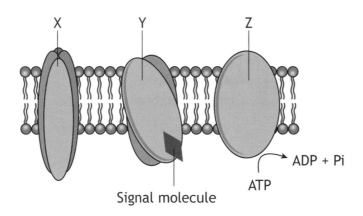

(a) Name a substance whose molecules can pass through the phospholipid bilayer.   1

_____

_____

(b) (i) Protein **X** represents aquaporin.

Name the substance this protein transports and describe how its molecules move through the channel.   2

_____

_____

_____

(ii) Protein **Y** is a gated channel controlled by a signal molecule as shown.

Give one other type of gated channel which can occur in phospholipid membranes.   1

_____

_____

(iii) State the role of ATP in the action of transporter protein **Z**.   1

_____

_____

MARKS | DO NOT WRITE IN THIS MARGIN

4. The chart below describes stages in the production of monoclonal antibody.

Stage description	Diagram
Stage 1 B lymphocytes obtained from treated mice and fusion with mouse melanoma cells attempted	B lymphocyte melanoma cell
Stage 2 Resulting cells transferred to plastic wells containing selective medium and supernatant fluid screened for presence of desired antibody	
Stage 3 Cells selected from wells with desired antibody isolated and cloned	
Stage 4 Desired antibody isolated and used in medical procedures	

(a) Describe how mice would be treated prior to **Stage 1** so that they would produce the required B lymphocytes.   1

_____

_____

(b) Explain why the mouse B lymphocytes must be hybridised with melanoma cells in **Stage 1**.   1

_____

_____

(c) Give **two** uses of monoclonal antibodies in medical procedures.   2

_____

_____

_____

MARKS | DO NOT WRITE IN THIS MARGIN

5. In multicellular organisms, the process of apoptosis in target cells is triggered by cell death signals, which may originate within or outwith the cell. The flow chart below shows the events triggered by a cell death signal from outwith the cell.

| Cell death signal molecules released from a lymphocyte | → | Signal molecule binds to surface receptor on target cell | → | Degrading enzymes in target cell activated | → | Target cell destroyed |

(a) Give **one** reason why programmed cell death initiated by a lymphocyte can be beneficial to multicellular organisms.

1

(b) (i) Name **two** degrading enzymes activated during apoptosis.

2

(ii) Bcl-2 is a regulator protein which can inhibit apoptosis. In humans this protein is encoded by the BCL2 gene. Mutations in this gene can increase the levels of Bcl-2.

Suggest why these mutations are usually associated with tumour growth.

2

(c) Give **one** example of an event originating within a cell which can trigger apoptosis.

1

6. Describe non-specific defences against disease in mammals.

4

_____

_____

_____

_____

_____

_____

MARKS | DO NOT WRITE IN THIS MARGIN

7. The ruff, *Philomachus pugnax*, is a medium-sized ground-nesting wading bird. Males display and fight for females during the breeding season at a grassy site called a lek. There are two male forms: territorial males with conspicuous dark plumage and satellite males with conspicuous light plumage. Territorial males occupy and defend the best mating territories in the lek. Satellite males don't hold territory but enter leks and attempt to mate with females visiting those territories occupied by territorial males. The presence of both types of male in a territory attracts additional females. Females are polygamous and lack the conspicuous plumage of males.

(a) State the term used to describe structural differences between males and females of the same species.   1

(b) Explain the selective advantages which each type of male ruff gains in securing mating opportunities with females.

   (i) Territorial male   1

   (ii) Satellite male   1

(c) (i) Describe what is meant by the term polygamous.   1

   (ii) Explain the advantage to female ruff of having inconspicuous plumage.   1

MARKS | DO NOT WRITE IN THIS MARGIN

8. *Prestonella bowkeri* is a small terrestrial snail found in rocky cliff face habitats on the Great Escarpment of southern Africa. The species lives in cracks and crevices on cliffs, as shown in the diagram below, where it can be reliably located and is easy to catch.

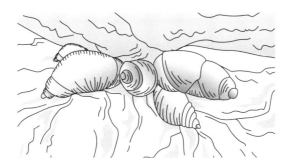

In an attempt to estimate how its population changes at one small cliff site, samples of snails were captured, marked and released on two separate occasions during a year of study, as shown in the table below.

Date of sampling	Number of snails captured and marked during sampling (M)	Number of snails in second sample (C)	Number of marked snails in second sample (R)	Population estimate (N)
March	1435	1725	195	–
September	1400	–	250	7000

(a) Use the population estimate formula N = MC/R to

  (i) calculate the population estimate for the March sample;　　1

   Space for calculation

   _____

  (ii) calculate the number of the snails in the April sample.　　1

   Space for calculation

   _____

MARKS | DO NOT WRITE IN THIS MARGIN

8. (continued)

(b)   (i)   Describe an appropriate sampling method for a slow-moving mollusc with predictable behaviour at a small site such as this.   **2**

_____

_____

_____

(ii)   Suggest an appropriate method for marking individual snails, and describe factors which should be considered when choosing the method to be used.   **2**

_____

_____

_____

MARKS | DO NOT WRITE IN THIS MARGIN

9. *Cyanea* is a genus of endemic flowering plants on the Hawaiian islands. *Cyanea* is thought to have co-evolved with species of Hawaiian honeycreepers and honeyeaters, which serve as pollinators of their flowers. The birds visit flowers to obtain nectar from nectaries within the bases of the flower tubes. As the birds probe the flowers with their beaks, pollen is brushed onto the feathering of their heads and can be carried to the next flower and rubbed off onto its stigmas. The diagram below shows the curvature and length of the flower tubes of two different *Cyanea* species and the heads of their main pollinators.

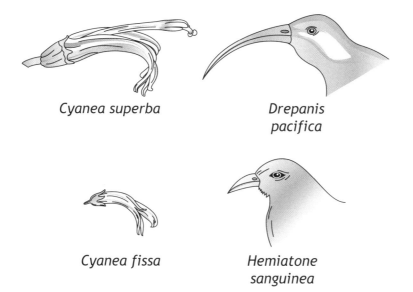

Cyanea superba   Drepanis
                          pacifica

Cyanea fissa   Hemiatone
                          sanguinea

(a) Explain what is meant by the term co-evolved.   1

_____

_____

(b) Explain the advantage to *Drepanis pacifica* of its relationship with *Cyanea superba*.   2

_____

_____

_____

(c) Describe how the Red Queen hypothesis can be used to explain the co-evolution of plants and their pollinators.   2

_____

_____

_____

MARKS | DO NOT WRITE IN THIS MARGIN

10. The dipper, *Cinclus cinclus*, is a small bird which lives by fast-flowing rocky streams in northern and western Britain. The birds feed on invertebrates which they pick from beneath the water surface. They build their nests on ledges or under rocky overhangs on steep river banks.

Dippers breed comparatively early in the year but the date of egg-laying varies. During 1987, observers in Wales monitored pairs of breeding dippers and recorded the date on which their first egg was laid. The pH of the water in the nest area was also measured. The graph below shows the results of their investigation.

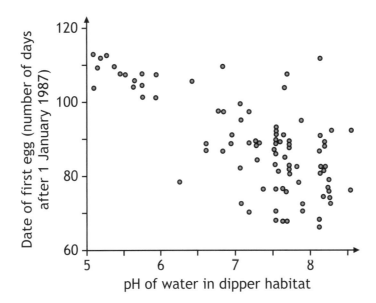

pH of water in dipper habitat

It was concluded that the less acidic the water in their habitat, the earlier in the year the birds' egg-laying date.

(a) The hypothesis being tested in the investigation above is that water pH affects egg-laying date in dippers.

Suggest **two** other factors which might be affecting egg-laying date in this species.

2

_____

_____

_____

MARKS | DO NOT WRITE IN THIS MARGIN

10. **(continued)**

(b) (i) The data can be attributed to correlation or causation.

From the data given, decide which you agree with and tick the appropriate box.

correlation ☐   causation ☐

Explain the reason for your choice.   **2**

_____

_____

_____

_____

_____

(ii) Compare the relationship between the pH of water or egg-laying date on pH 5.0—6.0 or pH 7.0—8.0.   **1**

_____

_____

_____

(c) Suggest **one** factor related to the validity and **one** factor related to the reliability of the experimental design which would have to be taken into account when making conclusions from the results.   **2**

Validity _____

_____

Reliability _____

_____

MARKS | DO NOT WRITE IN THIS MARGIN

11. Answer **either A or B** in the space below.

A   Describe the primary, secondary, tertiary and quaternary levels of protein structure.   **8**

OR

B   Describe the role of photoreceptors in triggering a nervous impulse in animal eyes.   **8**

Space for answer

[END OF MODEL PAPER]

ADDITIONAL SPACE FOR ANSWERS AND ROUGH WORK

MARKS | DO NOT WRITE IN THIS MARGIN

ADDITIONAL SPACE FOR ANSWERS AND ROUGH WORK

MARKS | DO NOT WRITE IN THIS MARGIN

ADVANCED HIGHER FOR CfE

Model Paper 3

Whilst this Model Paper has been specially commissioned by Hodder Gibson for use as practice for the Advanced Higher (for Curriculum for Excellence) exams, the key reference document remains the SQA Specimen Paper 2015.

National
Qualifications
MODEL PAPER 3

Biology
Section 1—Questions

Duration — 2 hours 30 minutes

Instructions for the completion of Section 1 are given on *Page two* of your question and answer booklet.

Record your answers on the answer grid on *Page three* of your question and answer booklet.

Before leaving the examination room you must give your question and answer booklet to the Invigilator; if you do not, you may lose all the marks for this paper.

HODDER
GIBSON
LEARN MORE

SECTION 1 — 25 marks

Attempt ALL questions

1. The diagram below shows a haemocytometer counting chamber containing a sample from a culture of animal cells. The depth of the chamber is 0·01 cm.

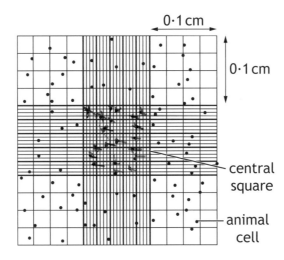

The concentration of cells in this culture, based on the cell count from the central square, is

A $2·0 \times 10^4$ cells per cm^3

B $2·0 \times 10^5$ cells per cm^3

C $2·0 \times 10^6$ cells per cm^3

D $2·0 \times 10^7$ cells per cm^3.

2. The graphs below show the effect of plant growth regulators on the development of roots and shoots in plant tissue culture.

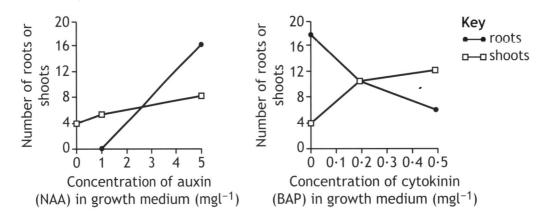

Which of the following treatments produces a root : shoot ratio of 2 : 1?

A $0·2\,mgl^{-1}$ BAP

B $0·5\,mgl^{-1}$ BAP

C $2\,mgl^{-1}$ NAA

D $5\,mgl^{-1}$ NAA

3. R groups of amino acids, which are polar, acidic and basic, are attracted to water molecules in the cytoplasm of cells and are therefore described as

   A   charged

   B   hydrophilic

   C   ionised

   D   hydrophobic.

4. Each molecule of oxygen that binds to a sub-unit of haemoglobin has the effect of increasing the affinity of the remaining sub-units to oxygen.

   This type of interaction is called

   A   co-operativity

   B   facilitated transport

   C   induced fit

   D   positive modulation.

5. Which of the following is **not** a function of Na/KATPase?

   A   maintaining the osmotic balance in animal cells

   B   phosphorylating channel proteins

   C   generating the ion gradient for glucose symports

   D   maintaining resting potential of membranes

6. A hydrophobic signalling molecule diffuses into a cell through a

   A   carrier protein

   B   receptor protein

   C   phospholipid bilayer

   D   transmembrane channel.

7. The catalytic power of an enzyme can be compared by measuring values called Kcat and Km.

   If Kcat divided by Km gives a value between 10^8 and 10^9 units, then the enzyme's activity is said to have reached "catalytic perfection".

   The enzyme acetylcholinesterase has a Kcat of $1{\cdot}4 \times 10^4$ and a Km of 9×10^{-5} units.

   Which line in the table below is correct for this enzyme?

	Value of Kcat/ Km (units)	Activity has reached catalytic perfection
A	$1{\cdot}6 \times 10^8$	yes
B	$6{\cdot}4 \times 10^8$	yes
C	$1{\cdot}6 \times 10^8$	no
D	$6{\cdot}4 \times 10^8$	no

8. *Paclitaxel* and *Cisplatin* are chemotherapy drugs used in the treatment of some cancers. *Paclitaxel* inhibits spindle formation and *Cisplatin* interferes with DNA replication.

   Which line in the table below shows the phases of the cell cycle in which these drugs would act effectively?

	Chemotherapy drug	
	Paclitaxel	Cisplatin
A	G2	S
B	M	G1
C	S	M
D	M	S

9. Which of the following is **not** a substrate for caspases?

   A   DNA

   B   actin

   C   histone

   D   tubulin

10. The quantity of a specific protein in a food sample can be estimated using monoclonal antibodies, as shown in the diagram below.

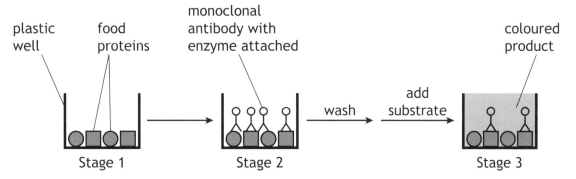

Stage 1 — A sample of food is added to a plastic well and proteins stick to the plastic base.

Stage 2 — Monoclonal antibodies with attached enzyme are added and these bind to the specific protein.

Stage 3 — Substrate for the enzyme is added, which is then converted to a coloured product, the intensity of which indicates the quantity of the specific protein present.

Which line in the table of results below shows correctly the effect on the protein estimate and the reason for this effect if the procedure were carried out without the wash between Stages 2 and 3?

	Effect on protein estimate	*Reason for effect*
A	underestimate	more substrate converted to product
B	underestimate	less substrate converted to product
C	overestimate	more substrate converted to product
D	overestimate	less substrate converted to product

11. In the production of monoclonal antibodies, myeloma cells are fused with B-lymphocytes to form hybridomas.

B-lymphocytes are used in this process

A   so that the hybridomas are prompted to divide continuously

B   because each lymphocyte can produce several different antibodies

C   so that the selection of successfully hybridised cells is easier

D   because each lymphocyte is limited to the production of one type of antibody.

12. Which line in the table below identifies features of cone cells from human eyes?

	Are able to function in low light intensity	Contain different forms of opsin in their photoreceptor proteins compared to rod cells	Photoreceptor protein contains retinal
A	yes	yes	no
B	no	yes	yes
C	no	no	no
D	yes	no	yes

13. Which of the following statements about the sodium–potassium pump is **correct**?

A   The transport protein has an affinity for sodium ions in the cytoplasm.

B   It results in a higher concentration of sodium inside the cell.

C   The transport protein has an affinity for sodium ions in the extracellular fluid.

D   It results in a higher concentration of potassium ions outside the cell.

14. Which of the following **cannot** be the result of interspecific competition?

A   occupation of a realised niche by a species

B   competitive exclusion of a species

C   occupation of a fundamental niche by a species

D   co-existence of species by resource partitioning

Questions 15 and 16 refer to the following information.

The two spot ladybird, *Adalia bipunctata*, occurs in the Birmingham area of England where there are non-melanic and melanic forms. The species lives on greenfly found on the lime trees, which occur at distinct sites in the area.

To investigate the hypothesis that the frequencies of melanic individuals have been decreased by increased sunshine levels produced by reduced smoke pollution in the atmosphere, investigators collected data over many years from three sites in the area in which lime trees occur. The ladybirds from different sites are free to interbreed because of winged stages in their life cycle.

Some of the results of the investigation are shown in the graph below.

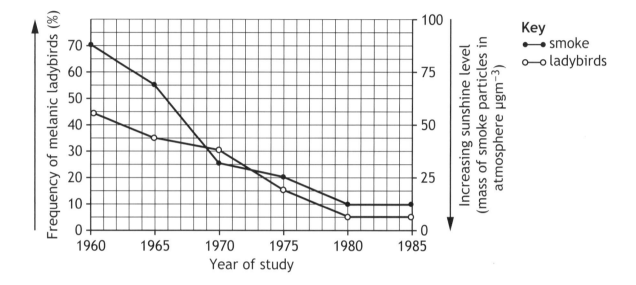

15. Which is the independent variable under investigation?

   A   mass of smoke

   B   sunshine level

   C   sample site location

   D   frequency of melanic forms

16. As can be seen from the graph, the frequency of the allele which causes melanism in *Adalia bipunctata* has changed over the period of the investigation.

   Which of the following could **not** have caused this effect?

   A   selection pressure

   B   genetic drift

   C   sampling error

   D   free interbreeding

17. Which line in the table below describes the process of imprinting?

	Must develop within a critical period	Is reversible	Rate of learning process involved
A	yes	no	rapid
B	no	yes	slow
C	no	no	rapid
D	yes	yes	slow

18. Which of the following is a non-specific immune response to a parasite?

A   apoptosis induced by T-lymphocytes

B   presentation of antigens by phagocytes

C   production of antibodies by a B-lymphocyte clone

D   apoptosis induced by natural killer (NK) cells

19. Which line in the table below describes cells at the end of a meiotic stage?

	Meiotic stage	Chromosome complement of cells present at end of stage	Number of cells at end of stage
A	Meiosis I	haploid	4
B	Meiosis I	diploid	2
C	Meiosis II	haploid	4
D	Meiosis II	diploid	2

20. Which line in the table below identifies features of genetic drift?

	Type of process	Size of population most likely to be affected
A	random	large
B	non-random	small
C	non-random	large
D	random	small

21. In humans, some genes are present on the Y chromosome but not on the X chromosome. An allele of one of these genes causes a form of deafness.

What is the percentage chance of a male, with deafness caused by this allele, having a child who inherits the condition?

A   0%

B   25%

C   50%

D   100%

22. The arctic fox is a predator of barnacle geese. To reduce predation, geese are periodically vigilant, which means they look up from grazing to scan for foxes. In a study of this behaviour, different flock sizes of geese were monitored for the 10 minute period after a model fox was placed 100 m from the feeding flock. The percentage of time each individual spent with their head raised was recorded and the results are shown in the graph below.

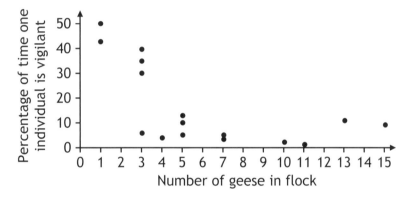

Which of the following procedures would be needed to test the hypothesis that vigilance behaviour of individual barnacle geese in response to the presence of foxes decreases as flock size increases?

A   Repeat the work and calculate the average results.

B   Repeat the work and increase the recording time to 20 minutes.

C   Repeat the work but get data for missing flock sizes.

D   Repeat the work but have trials with no model fox present.

23. Neutrophils are phagocytes found in mammal blood that have to be replaced in large numbers every day. The half-life of neutrophils is only 6 hours, which means that their number decreases by half in this period.

If a mammal stopped replacing its neutrophils, what percentage of its original number would remain after 24 hours?

A   0%

B   6%

C   13%

D   25%

24. The diagram below shows some details of the body of an individual nematode worm *Caenorhabditis elegans*.

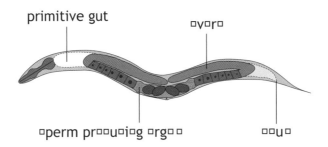

primitive gut

□v□r□

□perm pr□□u□i□g □rg□□   □□u□

The information given suggests that this individual is

A   parasitic

B   parthenogenic

C   hermaphroditic

D   sexually dimorphic.

25. Which line in the table below shows the meanings of terms used in the study of animal behaviour?

	Terms used in the study of animal behaviour		
	Latency	Frequency	Duration
A	time between the presentation of a stimulus and the behaviour it evokes	number of times a behaviour is performed in a set period	time over which a behaviour occurs
B	number of times a behaviour is performed in a set period	time between the presentation of a stimulus and the behaviour it evokes	time over which a behaviour occurs
C	time between the presentation of a stimulus and the behaviour it evokes	time over which a behaviour occurs	number of times a behaviour is performed in a set period
D	time over which a behaviour occurs	number of times a behaviour is performed in a set period	time between the presentation of a stimulus and the behaviour it evokes

[END OF SECTION 1. NOW ATTEMPT THE QUESTIONS IN SECTION 2
OF YOUR QUESTION AND ANSWER BOOKLET]

AH

National Qualifications
MODEL PAPER 3

Mark

Biology
Section 1 — Answer Grid and Section 2

Duration — 2 hours 30 minutes

Fill in these boxes and read what is printed below.

Full name of centre

Town

Forename(s)

Surname

Number of seat

Date of birth

Day	Month	Year	Scottish candidate number

Total marks — 90

SECTION 1 — 25 marks

Attempt ALL questions.

Instructions for completion of Section 1 are given on *Page two*.

SECTION 2 — 65 marks

Attempt ALL questions.

Write your answers clearly in the spaces provided in this booklet. Additional space for answers and rough work is provided at the end of this booklet. If you use this space you must clearly identify the question number you are attempting. Any rough work must be written in this booklet. You should score through your rough work when you have written your final copy.

Use **blue** or **black** ink.

Before leaving the examination room you must give this booklet to the Invigilator; if you do not you may lose all the marks for this paper.

SECTION 1— 25 marks

The questions for Section 1 are contained on *Page 115*—Questions.
Read these and record your answers on the answer grid on *Page 129* opposite.
Use **blue** or **black** ink. Do NOT use gel pens or pencil.

1. The answer to each question is **either** A, B, C or D. Decide what your answer is, then fill in the appropriate bubble (see sample question below).

2. There is **only one correct** answer to each question.

3. Any rough working should be done on the additional space for answers and rough work at the end of this booklet.

Sample Question

The thigh bone is called the

    A   humerus

    B   femur

    C   tibia

    D   fibula.

The correct answer is **B**—femur. The answer **B** bubble has been clearly filled in (see below).

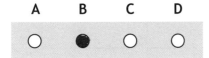

Changing an answer

If you decide to change your answer, cancel your first answer by putting a cross through it (see below) and fill in the answer you want. The answer below has been changed to **D**.

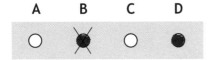

If you then decide to change back to an answer you have already scored out, put a tick (✓) to the **right** of the answer you want, as shown below:

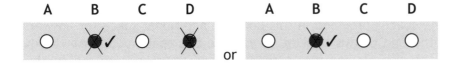

SECTION 1 — Answer Grid

	A	B	C	D
1	○	○	○	○
2	○	○	○	○
3	○	○	○	○
4	○	○	○	○
5	○	○	○	○
6	○	○	○	○
7	○	○	○	○
8	○	○	○	○
9	○	○	○	○
10	○	○	○	○
11	○	○	○	○
12	○	○	○	○
13	○	○	○	○
14	○	○	○	○
15	○	○	○	○
16	○	○	○	○
17	○	○	○	○
18	○	○	○	○
19	○	○	○	○
20	○	○	○	○
21	○	○	○	○
22	○	○	○	○
23	○	○	○	○
24	○	○	○	○
25	○	○	○	○

SECTION 2 — 65 marks

Attempt ALL questions

It should be noted that question 10 contains a choice.

1. The red grouse, *Lagopus lagopus scoticus*, is a game bird which occupies moorland habitats in Scotland. The birds may be infected by the endoparasitic helminth worm *Trichostrongylus tenuis*. Adult worms live in the birds' guts, and larval stages of the worm pass out in faeces. Mature larvae climb heather stems and may be eaten by grouse, which then become infected.

    The sizes of the grouse population in a study area were recorded each spring over a 10 year period between 1976 and 1986. Samples of the birds were caught in the autumn of each year and the average number of worms per bird determined.

    The results are shown in **Figure 1**.

    Figure 1: Size of grouse population in spring and average number of worms per bird in autumn

    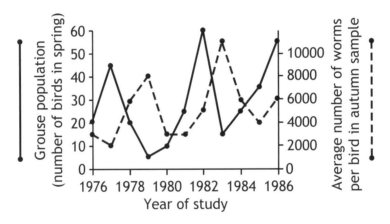

    Half of the captured birds in each autumn sample were treated with a drug to remove the parasitic worms, and the other half were left untreated to act as a control. All birds in the samples were weighed and marked before being released. Some of these birds were recaptured the following spring and reweighed before being released again. The results are shown in **Table 1**.

    Table 1: Average masses of red grouse in samples

Sample of grouse	Average mass (kg)
Birds caught in autumn	0·720
Treated bird recaptured the following spring	0·815
Untreated bird recaptured the following spring	0·756

MARKS | DO NOT WRITE IN THIS MARGIN

1. (continued)

The breeding success of birds marked in 1981 was determined over the following three years by counting the average number of chicks they produced as shown in **Figure 2**.

Figure 2: Breeding success of marked birds 1982—84

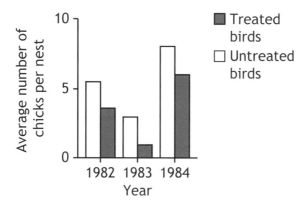

A computer simulation model of the effects on grouse and parasite populations of treating different percentages of grouse populations in spring with the drug was undertaken. **Figure 3** shows the results of this simulation.

Figure 3: Results of simulation model of the effects of treating different percentages of a grouse population with the drug

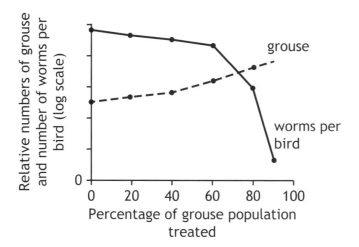

(a) It has been hypothesised that the population cycles of red grouse in Scotland are caused by the effect of the parasitic worm infection.

(i) Describe evidence from **Figure 1** which supports this hypothesis.   1

_____

_____

(ii) Describe additional types of evidence which would be needed to provide further support to the hypothesis.   1

_____

_____

MARKS | DO NOT WRITE IN THIS MARGIN

1. (continued)

(b) Describe the effect of the drug treatment on the mass of grouse shown in **Table 1** and suggest an explanation for this effect.   **2**

_____

_____

_____

(c) (i) Describe the effect of infection with parasitic worms on the reproductive success of the grouse shown in **Figure 2** and suggest an explanation for this effect.   **2**

_____

_____

_____

(ii) Give **one** piece of evidence which indicates that worm infection is not the only factor which affects the reproductive success of grouse.   **1**

_____

_____

(d) (i) From **Figure 3**, describe what happens to the number of grouse as the percentage of the population treated by the drug is increased.

Give full explanations for this.   **3**

_____

_____

_____

_____

(ii) Treating the entire population of grouse in the study with this drug is unlikely to ensure that the study area will be completely free of parasites in the following year.

Give **two** reasons for this.   **2**

_____

_____

_____

2. Haemoglobin is a protein found within the red blood cells of humans and other vertebrates.

  (a) The diagram below shows the structure of a molecule of haemoglobin. The molecule consists of four globular protein sub-units, each of which is bound to a haem group that contains an iron atom.

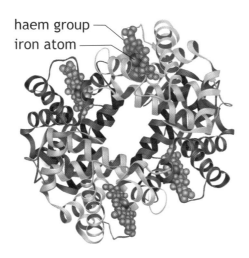

haem group —
iron atom —

    (i) With reference to the haemoglobin molecule, describe what is meant by the quaternary structure of a protein.

                            1

    (ii) Give the term used to describe non-protein groups, such as haem, which are tightly bound to proteins and are essential for their function.

                            1

MARKS | DO NOT WRITE IN THIS MARGIN

2. (continued)

(b) The graph below shows how the binding of oxygen to human haemoglobin is affected by the partial pressure of oxygen and the pH in its surroundings.

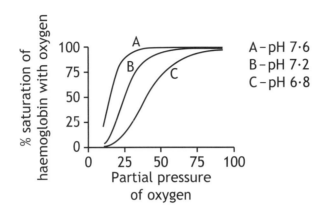

(i) Explain how the principle of positive co-operativity can account for the general similarity in the shape of the three graphs.

1

_____

_____

(ii) Graph line C represents the % saturation of haemoglobin with oxygen in muscle tissue.

1   Name **two** substances produced by respiring muscle cells which would reduce pH.

2

_____

_____

2   Explain why the change in % saturation of haemoglobin with O_2 in lower pH is an advantage in muscle tissue.

2

_____

_____

3   Apart from lowering the pH, give **one** other factor which could cause the O_2 binding curve of haemoglobin to shift to the right.

1

_____

MARKS | DO NOT WRITE IN THIS MARGIN

3. The alpha helical structure of a molecule of the protein histone 4 (H4) is shown in **Figure 1**.

Figure 2 represents three nucleosomes from a eukaryotic cell, showing the histone molecules which make up their core.

Figure 1: Structure of protein H4

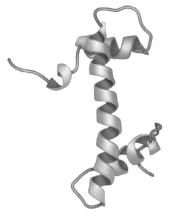

Figure 2: Nucleosomes from a eukaryotic cell

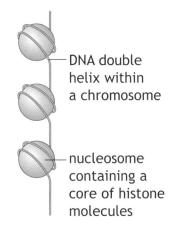

DNA double helix within a chromosome

nucleosome containing a core of histone molecules

(a) (i) Name the type of bonding which maintains the alpha helix shape of the protein H4.

1

(ii) Identify the level of protein structure shown by the alpha helix in **Figure 1**.

1

(b) Describe the importance of nucleosomes to DNA organisation and the functioning of eukaryotic cells.

1

(c) Over 20% of the amino acids found in histones are the positively charged lysine and arginine.

Explain the significance of the abundance of these positively charged amino acids to the formation of a nucleosome.

1

MARKS | DO NOT WRITE IN THIS MARGIN

4. The diagram below represents the cell cycle which consists of interphase (G1, S and G2), mitosis and cytokinesis (M). The cycle is regulated by checkpoints in G1, G2 and M as shown in the diagram. If the signal to go ahead is not received at the end of G1, the cell may switch to a non-dividing state called the G0 phase.

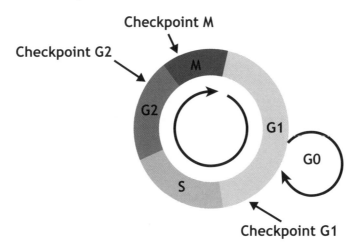

(a) (i) Cell cycle rates can vary.

        State the probable results of both uncontrolled increases and decreases in the rates of the cell cycle.   2

        _____

        _____

        _____

    (ii) Describe what happens to a cell during the cytokinesis stage of the M phase.   1

        _____

        _____

MARKS | DO NOT WRITE IN THIS MARGIN

4. (continued)

(b) The flow chart below shows events which lead up to checkpoint G1.

| During G1, cyclins accumulate | → | Cyclins activate kinases (Cdks) | → | Activated kinases (Cdks) phosphorylate retinoblastoma (Rb) | → | Phosphorylated Rb signals S phase to proceed |

(i) Give **one** change which occurs in a cell as it moves through G1, which leads to an accumulation of cyclins.

1

_____

_____

(ii) Explain the role of transcription in the early part of the S phase.

2

_____

_____

_____

MARKS | DO NOT WRITE IN THIS MARGIN

5. Describe the various forms of channel protein which occur in the membranes of cells.

4

6. The common dandelion, *Taraxacum officinale*, is a plant species which shows geographic parthenogenesis. The plants can be parasitised by rust fungi of the order *Pucciniales*.

Populations of dandelions along a line of increasing latitude in central Europe, as shown in the map below, were studied. The percentages of parthenogenic plants and the incidence of infection by rust fungi were determined, and the results are shown in the table below.

Map

Table

Transect point	% of parthenogenic plants	Incidence of parasitic rust infection (% plants infected)
1	18	48·0
2	15	54·0
3	48	3·0
4	100	0·0
5	100	5·0

(a) State what is meant by the term parthenogenesis.   1

_____

_____

MARKS

6. (continued)

(b)   (i) Suggest an abiotic factor which may vary with latitude from south to north.   1

_____

(ii) Describe how this abiotic factor could be measured.   1

_____

_____

(c) From the data in the **table**, describe how the incidence of parthenogenic plants varies with the incidence of rust infection.   1

_____

_____

(d) Give a hypothesis which would explain the relationship between the parasite, parthenogenesis and the latitude of populations of dandelion.   2

_____

_____

_____

MARKS | DO NOT WRITE IN THIS MARGIN

7. (a) The marine worm *Bonellia viridis* lives in burrows and crevices in the sea bed where it feeds using its proboscis, which can extend out around the burrow. Unoccupied burrows and suitable crevices are in short supply. The larvae of this species are not sexually differentiated. If a larva settles onto the sea bed, it differentiates into a female and competes for a burrow in which it develops a body, as shown in the diagram below. If a larva settles near to an already differentiated female worm, it is taken into the female's body where it differentiates into a 1—3 mm male. The male lives within the female's body and provides sperm to fertilise her eggs, which are later released into the water.

Female worm (life size)   Male worm (×10)

proboscis

   (i) From the information given, explain the advantage to the worm of environmental sex determination.   **2**

   _____

   _____

   _____

   (ii) Suggest a mechanism by which a larva could detect the presence of a female already in a burrow.   **1**

   _____

   _____

   (iii) Suggest how the adult male worms obtain food.   **1**

   _____

   _____

(b) Sex in *Bonellia* is determined by environmental factors. Other organisms have different mechanisms for the determination of sex.

   Describe the basis of the genetic determination of sex in *Drosophila*.   **1**

   _____

   _____

8. The diagram below shows features of a retrovirus.

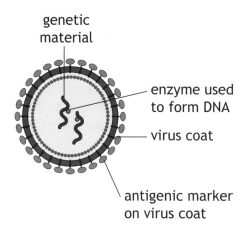

genetic material

enzyme used to form DNA

virus coat

antigenic marker on virus coat

(a) Name the enzyme used by retroviruses to form DNA.   1

_____

_____

(b) Describe how retroviruses affect the genotype of eukaryotic cells.   1

_____

_____

(c) (i) Explain how the variation of the antigenic markers on the coat of this virus can make the design of vaccines against it difficult.   1

_____

_____

(ii) Explain what is meant by the term "herd immunity threshold".   1

_____

_____

MARKS | DO NOT WRITE IN THIS MARGIN

9. Phosphorylase is an enzyme found in potato tuber cell cytoplasm. It converts glucose-1-phosphate (G1P) to starch, which is stored in grains in the tuber cells as shown in the diagram below.

cytoplasm with phosphorylase

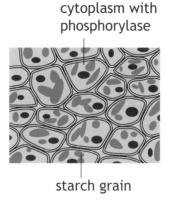

starch grain

In an experiment aiming to compare concentration of the enzyme, starch-free phosphorylase extracts were prepared from random samples of the tubers of three different potato varieties using identical preparation procedures. Standard volumes of the extracts were mixed with standard volumes of G1P, and the time taken for starch molecules to be formed was measured. Several replicates for each potato variety were done and the results averaged.

As a positive control, a solution of commercially available phosphorylase was also tested.

The results are shown in the table below.

Phosphorylase source	Average time to convert $1\,cm^3$ of 1% G1P to starch (s)
Variety 1 extract	240
Variety 2 extract	230
Variety 3 extract	270
Commercial phosphorylase solution	150

(a) (i) Identify the independent variable in this experiment.   1

_____

(ii) Identify a potentially confounding variable in this experiment.   1

_____

MARKS | DO NOT WRITE IN THIS MARGIN

9.   **(continued)**

(b)   (i)   Explain what is meant by a positive control.   **1**

_____

_____

(ii)   Suggest how a negative control for this experiment could be designed.   **1**

_____

_____

(c)   Explain why it was important to ensure that the extracts were free of starch.   **1**

_____

_____

(d)   (i)   Potato varieties were sampled randomly.

Suggest how stratified sampling of the potato varieties could be done and how that would improve experimental validity.   **2**

_____

_____

_____

(ii)   Comment on the reliability of the experimental method.   **1**

_____

_____

10. Answer **either A or B** in the space below.

   A   Describe laboratory separation techniques used in the separation of amino acids and proteins.   **8**

   OR

   B   Describe how phosphate groups can alter protein structure and function.   **8**

Space for answer

[END OF MODEL PAPER]

ADDITIONAL SPACE FOR ANSWERS AND ROUGH WORK

ADDITIONAL SPACE FOR ANSWERS AND ROUGH WORK

ADDITIONAL SPACE FOR ANSWERS AND ROUGH WORK

MARKS | DO NOT WRITE IN THIS MARGIN

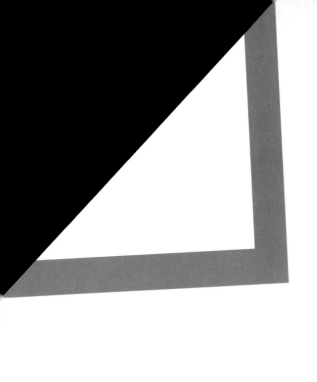

SQA AND HODDER GIBSON ADVANCED HIGHER FOR CfE BIOLOGY 2015

ADVANCED HIGHER FOR CfE BIOLOGY
SPECIMEN QUESTION PAPER

Section 1

Question	Response	Mark
1.	A	1
2.	C	1
3.	B	1
4.	A	1
5.	D	1
6.	B	1
7.	C	1
8.	A	1
9.	C	1
10.	A	1
11.	C	1
12.	D	1
13.	C	1
14.	D	1
15.	A	1
16.	B	1
17.	C	1
18.	D	1
19.	B	1
20.	D	1
21.	D	1
22.	B	1
23.	A	1
24.	D	1
25.	C	1

Section 2

Question			Expected response	Max mark	Additional guidance
1.	(a)		Proteome	1	
	(b)		• Drosha not working • miRNA/precursor not processed/cut • No (micro)RNA strand for RISC OR RISC can't bind (m)RNA • (RNA) interference reduced/translation is left on	2	Any two
	(c)	(i)	Cell growth/cell increases in mass	1	
		(ii)	62·5	1	
		(iii)	More KO cells in G1 and fewer in S (and G2 + M) (1) Differences are significant (only) in G1 and S/error bars don't overlap in G1 and S (1) OR If comparing only G1 bars or only S bars, then must point out significant difference (1)	2	Comparison can be made via data but data must be correct
	(d)	(i)	(After induction of differentiation) • in KO cells it is (generally) lower than normal cells • it increases in normal cells (over time) • in KO cells + one from below — no trend — decreases from day 8 — increases (to day 8) then decreases (It = expression = level of marker)	1	Any one
		(ii)	• In normal cells, as differentiation increases self-renewal decreases **OR** converse (must link the two graphs/processes) • In KO/abnormal cells, **both** processes decrease after day 8 • in KO/abnormal cells, **both** processes increase to day 8 • in KO/abnormal cells, self-renewal remains higher and differentiation remains lower **than normal**	2	Any two
2.	(a)		• GABA is a ligand/substance that can bind to protein • The channel is a protein that opens in response to GABA/ligand binding • Chloride passes through the protein when GABA is bound	2	Any two
	(b)		Transduction	1	
	(c)	(i)	Chloride movement is (generally) greater at any GABA conc. if drug present	1	
		(ii)	Changes the conformation of the GABA site	1	
		(iii)	(Make the cell more negative inside so) increase the membrane potential	1	

Question			Expected response	Max mark	Additional guidance
3.	(a)		Concentration of ATP solution	1	
	(b)	(i)	Freshness of meat/whether meat has been frozen/ temperature of storage/incubation time/time before measurement/thickness of strip	1	Any one
		(ii)	• Storage of meat may cause damage to muscle proteins so muscle contraction would be less with less fresh meat • Freezing meat may damage muscle fibres so less contraction would be measured • Freezing meat may preserve muscle proteins so more contraction would be measured • As storage temperature increases protein damage may increase so less muscle contraction would be measured • Increasing incubation time/time before measurement will give more time for ATP to diffuse so more muscle contraction would be measured • ATP will diffuse more slowly through thicker strips which could mean the solution does not reach all the fibres so less contraction will be measured	1	Any one Explanation of effect must match with chosen confounding variable
	(c)		Not reliable (1) No independent replication/whole experiment was only carried out once OR Only one measurement for each chop at each concentration of ATP (1)	2	
	(d)		Negative control	1	
	(e)		May have prevented a representative sample being selected	1	
4.	(a)		The training will have no effect on GLUT 4 content of muscle	1	
	(b)		ND UT is baseline GLUT 4 **and** training does not produce significant increase (1) D UT is (significantly) lower GLUT 4 than baseline and exercise generates significant increase (1)	2	
	(c)		Type 1 diabetes is failure to produce insulin whereas type 2 diabetes is loss of insulin receptor function/ failure to respond to insulin	1	
5.	(a)		Hydrophobic	1	
	(b)		Thyroxine receptor protein is blocking transcription/ thyroxine binding removes repression of genes (1) More NaKATPase in membrane so more energy expenditure/higher metabolic rate (1)	2	
	(c)	(i)	People need to be treated for several weeks before metabolic rate reaches normal	1	
		(ii)	Starting metabolic rate is different for each individual	1	

Question			Expected response	Max mark	Additional guidance
6.	(a)		Retinal	1	
	(b)		• Excited rhodopsin activates G protein which in turn activates many enzyme molecules • Enzyme molecules cause closure of ion channels/catalyse the removal of molecules that keep channels open • Inward leakage of positive ions/Na^+ and Ca^+ is halted so membrane potential increases • Hyperpolarisation/increasing charge stimulates nerve impulse	2	Any two
	(c)		Wide range of wavelengths absorbed/high degree of amplification from single photon	1	
7.	(a)		Men have one allele of the haemophilia gene whereas women have two alleles (of the haemophilia gene) **(1)** Recessive allele causing haemophilia not masked in men **(1)**	2	
	(b)		Daughter 100% **(1)** Son 50% **(1)**	2	
	(c)	(i)	Prevents a double dose of gene products (coded by the X chromosome) that might disrupt cellular function	1	
		(ii)	Inactivation of X chromosomes is random so this patient must have (by chance) more cells that have inactivated the unaffected allele/fewer cells that inactivated the affected allele	1	
8.			• homologous chromosomes pair (during meiosis I) • breakage and re-joining of DNA strands • at chiasmata • shuffles sections of DNA between homologous chromosomes • allows the recombination of alleles • (as) linked genes are separated	4	Any four
9.	(a)	(i)	Does not itself actively transmit parasite to another species	1	
		(ii)	Waterborne dispersal stage	1	
	(b)		• Mimic host antigens to evade detection • Modify host immune response to reduce chances of destruction • Antigenic variation allows rapid evolution to overcome host immune cell clonal selection	1	Any one
	(c)		Co-evolution of related species that interact frequently/closely **(1)** Change in traits of one species acts as a selection pressure on the other species **(1)**	2	

Question			Expected response	Max mark	Additional guidance
10.	(a)		300%	1	
	(b)	(i)	Reduction in abundance of named species due to increase in seal population/physical damage/trampling (1) Increase in abundance of *Prasiola crispa* due to reduced competition for space/greater tolerance of trampling (1)	2	
		(ii)	Loss of plants gives areas of bare rock OR Not all plant species counted	1	
	(c)	(i)	Carried out in a way that minimises impact on environment OR Consideration of rare/vulnerable species	1	
		(ii)	Population being sampled is split into sub-populations	1	
11.	A		1. Immune surveillance by white blood cells 2. T lymphocytes recognise antigens from pathogen 3. Antigens (from pathogen) displayed on the surface of infected cells 4. T lymphocytes destroy infected cells 5. T lymphocytes induce apoptosis 6. Phagocytes present antigens to lymphocytes 7. B lymphocytes produce specific antibodies 8. T lymphocytes/B lymphocytes amplified by clonal selection 9. A different lymphocyte is produced/selected for each antigen 10. Long-term survival of some members of T lymphocyte/B lymphocyte clones 11. Surviving lymphocytes act as immunological memory cells	8	Any eight
	B		1. Female choice assesses male fitness 2. Females assess honest signals (to assess fitness) 3. Fitness explained in terms of advantageous genes/low parasite burdens 4. Display behaviour of lekking species 5. Successful strategies of dominant and satellite males (in lekking species) 6. Example of lekking behaviour described 7. Male—male rivalry: large size/weaponry 8. Increases access to females through conflict 9. Behaviour of sneaker males 10. Importance of sign stimuli and fixed action pattern in birds/fish 11. Example of sign stimuli and fixed action pattern described	8	Any eight

ADVANCED HIGHER FOR CfE BIOLOGY MODEL PAPER 1

Section 1

Question	Response	Mark
1.	B	1
2.	D	1
3.	D	1
4.	C	1
5.	A	1
6.	B	1
7.	A	1
8.	B	1
9.	C	1
10.	A	1
11.	A	1
12.	D	1
13.	C	1
14.	D	1
15.	A	1
16.	A	1
17.	C	1
18.	D	1
19.	C	1
20.	B	1
21.	D	1
22.	B	1
23.	A	1
24.	C	1
25.	B	1

Section 2

Question			Expected response	Max mark
1.	(a)	(i)	Transmembrane protein	1
		(ii)	Four connected polypeptide sub-units	1
	(b)		To allow specific water molecules to be traced	1
	(c)	(i) 1	Rate of water molecule flow across the membrane increased when the AQP1 was activated	1
		(i) 2	Increase in rate of water molecule flow was **greater** when the concentration gradient was increased	1
		(ii)	There would be no net change in the mass of cells in isotonic solution	1
	(d)	(i)	Group 3 mice lose more water in their urine (than Group 1) **(1)** Because they do not have aquaporins (in their kidney tubule membranes) to reabsorb it **(1)**	2
		(ii)	Group 2 mice lose about the same body mass as Group 1 after a period without water **(1)** And the change in concentration of their urine (over the period) is about the same **(1)**	2
2.	(a)	(i)	99.7%	1
		(ii)	7 times	1
	(b)		When proteins (in solution) are brought to their isoelectric point, they have an overall neutral charge **(1)** and precipitate out of solution **(1)**	2
	(c)		Enzyme binds to the ligand and becomes trapped in the stationary phase/on the agarose **(1)** The stationary phase/agarose can then be washed and the (purified) enzyme released from entrapment/eluted **(1)**	2

Question			Expected response	Max mark
3.	(a)	(i)	The sequence of amino acids in the polypeptide chain	1
		(ii)	Alpha/α helix **(1)** Formed through H bonding between amino acids (in the polypeptide) **(1)**	2
	(b)		Rhodopsin molecules absorb light energy **(1)** And use it to pump protons/H⁺ across the membrane **(1)**	2
4.	(a)		Rhodopsin	1
	(b)	(i)	G-protein molecules activate (hundreds of) enzyme molecules	1
		(ii)	Allows animal to see in low light intensities/dim light	1
	(c)		Different forms of opsin (combine with retinal)	1
	(d)		Animals are sensitive to different colours/ wavelengths of light/can see in colour	1
5.	(a)		The binding of insulin to specific cell receptor molecules **(1)** triggers the recruitment of glucose transporter molecules/GLUTs to the membranes of fat and muscle cells **(1)**	2
	(b)	(i)	Diabetics have lower adiponectin levels so their cells not so sensitive to insulin **(1)** Lowered sensitivity to insulin makes cells less able to convert blood glucose to glycogen **(1)**	2
		(ii)	Lifestyle changes gave increased adiponectin levels **(1)** Drug treatment gave greater increases in adiponectin **(1)**	1
		(iii) 1	The potential effect of the treatments on the health of the individual volunteers	1

Question			Expected response	Max mark
		(iii) 2	Eliminate effects of variation between individuals **OR** Produce more reliable data	1
6.			1. Evolution is the change over time in the frequency of alleles in the gene pool of a population 2. Genetic drift is a random process 3. Named examples of random processes from: colonisation/ establishment of new populations/the founder effect; survivors of an environmental event/a volcanic eruption/an earthquake/a tsunami 4. A second named example 5. Genetic drift is more important in small populations (than large ones) 6. Alleles are more likely to be (completely) lost from the gene pool of a small population **[Any 4 for 1 mark each]**	4
7.	(a)	(i)	More likely to reveal nest sites than a random search	1
		(ii)	To minimise the effects of bias which may affect a non-random sample	1
	(b)		That feather mite infection does not affect the reproductive success of crested tits	1
	(c)		As the number of feather mites increases, the breeding success of birds is reduced	1
	(d)	(i)	As the size of the oil gland increases, the number of feather mites increases	1
		(ii)	Ensure that the measurements of oil gland size were made at the same time of day	1

Question			Expected response	Max mark
	(e)		Obtain correct licences **OR** ensure that as few individuals as possible are disturbed **OR** ensure that study sites are kept confidential **OR** do pilot studies to quantify the effect of disturbance on breeding success	1
8.	(a)		Intensity of *D. persimilis* is less than that of *D. pseudoobscura* (or converse) **AND** High intensity bursts are less frequent in *D. persimilis* (or converse)	1
	(b)	(i)	Females invest more than males in reproduction so it is more important to them to have successful mating	1
		(ii)	Those with the best/most attractive songs get most matings and produce most offspring (1) Song characteristics passed on to offspring (1)	2
9.	(a)	(i)	The population with no previous exposure to wasps was reduced when wasps were abundant but those with previous exposure increased their population in spite of the presence of wasps	1
		(ii)	A few already resistant flies survive the effects of parasitism and are able to breed (1) The resistant flies pass on their resistance to offspring and the incidence of resistance increases (1)	2
	(b)	(i)	Co-evolution occurs in pairs of species that interact frequently/closely	1
		(ii)	The wasp would evolve ways of overcoming the resistance and the population of flies would drop again	1

Question			Expected response	Max mark
10.	(a)	(i)	10 quadrats fail to show the number of species present in the area	1
		(ii)	25 quadrats waste resources because 20 is enough to show the same number of species in the area	1
	(b)		Ferns Conifers Flowering plants [Any 2 for 1 mark each]	2
11.	A		1. Meiosis occurs in diploid gamete mother cells 2. There are two phases: meiosis I and meiosis II 3. In meiosis I, homologous chromosomes pair 4. The paired chromosomes undergo crossing over at chiasmata 5. DNA is exchanged and recombination occurs 6. Homologous pairs are separated 7. In meiosis II, sister chromatids are separated 8. Haploid gametes form [Any 5 for 1 mark each] 9. In meiosis I, homologous chromosomes separate independently 10. And irrespective of their maternal and paternal origin 11. Chiasmata formation is random 12. New combinations of alleles on linked chromosome are formed [Any 3 for 1 mark each]	8

Question		Expected response	Max mark
	B	1. Genetic factors can determine sex 2. In live-bearing mammals sex chromosomes are involved 3. In mammals XX determines female/homogametic sex 4. In mammals XY determines male/heterogametic sex 5. The Y chromosome contains a gene/SRY which causes maleness 6. XY males lack the homologous alleles on their Y chromosome 7. In Drosophila the XY chromosome system is also involved 8. Environmental factors can determine sex **[Any 5 for 1 mark each]** 9. Sex can change within an individual as a result of size/age 10. Competition 11. Parasitic infection 12. Some species are hermaphroditic/have both sexes present in one individual **[Any 3 for 1 mark each]**	8

ADVANCED HIGHER FOR CfE BIOLOGY MODEL PAPER 2

Section 1

Question	Response	Mark
1.	B	1
2.	A	1
3.	A	1
4.	B	1
5.	C	1
6.	B	1
7.	A	1
8.	A	1
9.	C	1
10.	B	1
11.	D	1
12.	C	1
13.	D	1
14.	B	1
15.	A	1
16.	C	1
17.	B	1
18.	C	1
19.	C	1
20.	D	1
21.	A	1
22.	D	1
23.	A	1
24.	D	1
25.	D	1

Section 2

Question			Expected response	Max mark
1.	(a)		Glucose transport is greater in control red muscle cells than in control white muscle cells (1) When treated with insulin, glucose transport is increased more in red muscle cells than in white muscle cells (1)	2
	(b)		The standard error bars for red muscle and white muscle overlap showing that differences in average values are not significant	1
	(c)	(i)	High level of GLUT1 in plasma membrane and none in internal membranes before treatment	1
		(ii)	No effect on GLUT1 in plasma membrane **OR** Slight decrease in GLUT1 in plasma membrane	1
		(iii)	Decreases GLUT4 in plasma membrane and increases it in internal membranes in (both muscle types)	1
	(d)		Figure 3 shows that GLUT4 increases in the plasma membrane and decreases in the internal membranes in response to insulin (1) This change occurs in both muscle types but is greater in red than white muscle (1)	2
	(e)		In type 2 diabetes, insulin receptors are not so sensitive (1) So less GLUT4 is recruited into the plasma membrane (1)	2

Question			Expected response	Max mark
2.	(a)	(i)	Photon drives electron flow (1)	2
			And the energy from the electrons drives the H^+ flow (1)	
		(ii)	Diffusion (through protein X) down the concentration gradient	1
	(b)		ATP synthase (1)	2
			Allows the plant to trap energy in a chemical form/as ATP (1)	
3.	(a)		Oxygen/carbon dioxide/ others	1
	(b)	(i)	Water (1)	2
			Move from a high concentration to a lower concentration (1)	
		(ii)	Voltage-gated channels respond to changes in ion concentration	1
		(iii)	Phosphorylation provides energy for active transport (of sodium/potassium)	1
4.	(a)		Expose/immunise them to the appropriate antigen	1
	(b)		So that the hybrid makes antibodies specific to the appropriate antigen **AND** Produces an immortal cell line	1
	(c)		Prevention **OR** Diagnosis **OR** Treatment of disease **[Any 2 for 1 mark each]**	2
5.	(a)		Can kill infected cells	1
	(b)	(i)	DNAase (1) Proteinase/caspases (1)	2
		(ii)	Increased Bcl-2 so less inhibition of apoptosis (1) Tumour cells grow in the absence of apoptosis (1)	2
	(c)		DNA damage	1

Question			Expected response	Max mark
6.			1. Physical barriers such as skin/conjunctiva/ hair 2. Chemical secretions such as stomach acid/ mucus/tears/wax 3. Inflammatory responses 4. Phagocytosis/ phagocytes destroy(s) infected cells 5. Natural killer (NK) cells 6. Destroy abnormal cells **[Any 4 for 1 mark each]**	4
7.	(a)		Sexual dimorphism	1
	(b)	(i)	Occupy leks which are very attractive to females	1
		(ii)	Don't use energy defending territories but gain access to females that visit leks	1
	(c)	(i)	Mating with more than one partner	1
		(ii)	Makes her less easy to be seen by predators which raid the nests of ground-nesting birds	1
8.	(a)	(i)	12 694	1
		(ii)	1 250	1
	(b)	(i)	Systematic/methodical search (1) Over a set/defined time period (1)	2
		(ii)	That the paint should ultimately wear off/be non-indelible/ non-permanent (1) **OR** Choose different paint colours for different sampling times (1)	2
9.	(a)		Evolution in pairs of species which interact frequently/closely	1
	(b)		Reduction in competition for food/nectar (1) Only it has a beak that can reach the nectar within the *Cyanea superba* flowers (1)	2

Question			Expected response	Max mark
	(c)		Plant flower shape change provides selection pressure (1) Which acts on the pollinator to alter the direction of natural selection of beak length (1)	2
10.	(a)		Rainfall **OR** Temperature **OR** Invertebrate food availability (others) **[Any 2 for 1 mark each]**	2
	(b)	(i)	Correlation pH may be indirectly related to date of first egg (1) and may be caused by another variable such as rainfall/pollution (1) **OR** Causation pH is directly related to date of first egg (1) as shown by a line of best fit through the data points (1)	3
		(ii)	Between pH 5.0 and 6.0 there is a clear relationship between the pH and date of first egg **AND** between pH 7.0 and 8.0 no clear trend/ relationship can be seen between pH and date of first egg	2

Question			Expected response	Max mark
	(c)		Validity — effect of monitoring/disturbance on dipper behaviour **OR** Bias in the selection of nest to study, such as the remoteness of the nest sites (1) Reliability — number of birds studied **OR** Seasons involved **OR** Areas of the country covered (others) (1)	2
11.	A		1. Primary structure is the sequence of amino acids in the polypeptide 2. Secondary structure is the hydrogen bonding along the backbone 3–4. Which give alpha/α helices **OR** parallel/ antiparallel beta/β sheets **OR** beta/β turns **[Any 2]** 5. Folding of polypeptide into a tertiary structure 6. Caused by bonding through interactions between R groups in hydrophobic regions 7. And/or ionic bonds 8. van der Waals interactions 9. Disulfide bridges 10. Prosthetic groups are non-protein groups 11. Which bind tightly to protein and are necessary for its function 12. Quaternary structure is formed in proteins with several sub-units **[Any 8 for 1 mark each]**	8

Question			Expected response	Max mark
	B		1. Rhodopsin is the light-sensitive protein (in rod cells) 2. (Rhodopsin) is retinal combined with opsin 3. Cone cells are sensitive to specific/different wavelengths/colours 4. (In cone cells) different forms of opsin (combine with retinal) 5. Very high degree of amplification in rod cells 6. Results in sensitivity in low light intensities 7. Photon stimulates rhodopsin 8. A cascade of proteins amplifies the signal 9. Hundreds of G protein molecules are activated 10. This activates hundreds of molecules of enzyme 11. Enzymes generate product molecules 12. Sufficient product/threshold of product leads to a nerve impulse **[Any 8 for 1 mark each]**	8

ADVANCED HIGHER FOR CfE BIOLOGY MODEL PAPER 3

Section 1

Question	Response	Mark
1.	B	1
2.	D	1
3.	B	1
4.	A	1
5.	B	1
6.	C	1
7.	A	1
8.	B	1
9.	A	1
10.	C	1
11.	D	1
12.	B	1
13.	A	1
14.	C	1
15.	B	1
16.	D	1
17.	A	1
18.	D	1
19.	C	1
20.	D	1
21.	A	1
22.	C	1
23.	B	1
24.	C	1
25.	D	1

Section 2

Question			Expected response	Max mark
1.	(a)	(i)	The parasite population increases **following** an increase in the grouse population causing the grouse population to decrease again	1
		(ii)	Other key factors such as weather/predator numbers/other parasites/competition (would need to be investigated)	1
	(b)		Treated birds put on more mass (1) because their feeding does not have to support the parasite (1)	2
	(c)	(i)	Treated birds do better than untreated birds in terms of chicks raised over the following three years (1) The adult birds are in better condition/can obtain more food/can escape better from predators/resist the effects of other disease better (1)	2
		(ii)	The number of chicks produced by treated birds also varies from year to year	1
	(d)	(i)	As the percentage of treated birds increases, the number of grouse increases (1) Treated birds don't pass the parasite out in their eggs so there are less larval stages of worm in the heather (1) The treated birds breed better which increases their number **OR** Treated birds use less energy fighting parasites therefore breed better (1)	3
		(ii)	Immigration from other areas (1) Stages of the parasite remaining on heather stems and infecting the treated birds later (1)	2

Question			Expected response	Max mark
2.	(a)	(i)	The presence of sub-units bound together	1
		(ii)	Prosthetic groups	1
	(b)	(i)	As oxygen binds to one subgroup it enhances the affinity of the other groups for the oxygen	1
		(ii) 1	Lactic acid (1) Carbon dioxide (1)	2
		(ii) 2	The haemoglobin in graph C more readily releases oxygen in the muscle cells which have lower pH (1) Allowing them to respire more efficiently (1)	2
		(ii) 3	Increasing temperature	1
3.	(a)	(i)	Hydrogen	1
		(ii)	Secondary	1
	(b)		Keeps the DNA molecules from becoming twisted together which would prevent efficient transcription or replication **OR** Play a role in gene regulation	1
	(c)		Allow the histone molecules to bind with the negatively charged groups on DNA	1
4.	(a)	(i)	Increases could lead to tumour formation (1) Decreases could lead to degenerative disease (1)	2
		(ii)	The cytoplasm splits between the two daughter cells	1
	(b)	(i)	Increase in cell size	1
		(ii)	Transcription starts gene expression for enzymes (1) Enzymes/DNA polymerase/ligase have crucial roles in the replication of DNA (1)	2

Question			Expected response	Max mark
5.		1	1. Un-gated channels e.g. aquaporin 2. Changes in conformation can affect passive diffusion 3. Ligand gated channels 4. Are activated by signal molecules 5. Voltage gated channels 6. Are activated by changes in ion concentration **[Any 4 for 1 mark each]**	4
6.	(a)		Asexual reproduction in which offspring develop from unfertilised eggs	1
	(b)	(i)	Rainfall/humidity **OR** Temperature **OR** Photoperiod	1
		(ii)	Rainfall gauge **OR** Thermometer **OR** Sunshine recorder **OR** Weather station	1
	(c)		As the incidence of rust/fungal infection increases, the percentage of plants that are parthenogenic increases	1
	(d)		There are more rusts/fungi at lower latitudes which are warmer and more humid (1) At these latitudes sexual reproduction is favoured over parthenogenesis because it gives the variation needed to evolve with parasites (1)	2
7.	(a)	(i)	Ensures maximum occupation of available burrows/reduces competition for burrows (1) Increases chances of fertilisation of females (1)	2
		(ii)	Chemicals/substances/hormones/signal molecules released by females	1

Question			Expected response	Max mark
		(iii)	From the female/ parasitically	1
	(b)		Females have two X chromosomes and males have one X and one Y	1
8.	(a)		Reverse transcriptase	1
	(b)		Transcribe their RNA into DNA which joins into the host genome	1
	(c)	(i)	Antibodies produced against an antigenic marker will not be effective if the antigen changes its shape	1
		(ii)	The number of vaccinated individuals needed to stop an antigen spreading through a population	1
9.	(a)	(i)	Potato variety	1
		(ii)	Temperature OR pH OR Age/size of potato	1
	(b)	(i)	A control designed to show that a positive result can be obtained using the experimental method selected	1
		(ii)	A set of replicates without G1P OR With no enzyme source	1
	(c)		So that starch produced in the investigation/*de novo* starch could be identified	1
	(d)	(i)	Divide the tubers of one variety into age/size grouping based on criteria **(1)** Could remove confounding variables which could affect validity of conclusions **(1)**	2

Question			Expected response	Max mark
		(ii)	Method does not detail number/mass of tubers in the sample used OR Reliability low because only one extract per tuber variety tested OR Reliability could be improved by using more replicates/extracts	1
10.	A		1. Centrifugation 2. Separate a (solid) pellet from a (liquid) supernatant 3. Separated by differing density 4. Chromatography can be used to separate amino acids and proteins 5. Paper chromatography 6. Thin layer chromatography 7. Affinity chromatography 8. Electrophoresis 9. Uses current flowing through a buffer to separate proteins 10. Size and charge on proteins affects their migration through gels 11. At their isoelectric point proteins have neutral charge 12. And precipitate out of solution (at their isoelectric point) **[Any 8 for 1 mark each]**	8

Question		Expected response	Max mark
	B	1. Phosphate groups can be added or removed from R groups	8
		2. This can cause conformational change (to protein)	
		3. This change is reversible	
		4. Adding phosphate is a common post-translational modification	
		5. Many enzymes and receptors are regulated in this way	
		6. Kinases are (often) responsible for phosphorylating (other) proteins	
		7. Phosphatases catalyse dephosphorylation	
		8. Some proteins/ATPases use ATP for their phosphorylation	
		9. Myosin has heads that act as cross bridges when they bind actin	
		10. When ATP binds to myosin, the myosin head detaches from actin	
		11. The actin swings forward and rebinds	
		12. The rebinding releases ADP and a phosphate (group/ion) drags the myosin along the actin filament	
		[Any 8 for 1 mark each]	

Acknowledgements

Permission has been sought from all relevant copyright holders and Hodder Gibson is grateful for the use of the following:

Image © Artush/Shutterstock.com (SQP Section 2 page 19).

Hodder Gibson would like to thank SQA for use of any past exam questions that may have been used in model papers, whether amended or in original form.